MW00790358

BIG TEAM FARMS

BIG TEAM FARMS

GROWING FARMS DIFFERENTLY

Welcome to the Big Team!

Sarah K Mock

SARAH K MOCK

NEW DEGREE PRESS

COPYRIGHT © 2022 SARAH K MOCK

All rights reserved.

BIG TEAM FARMS

Growing Farms Differently

ISBN   979-8-88504-138-6 *Paperback*

          979-8-88504-771-5 *Kindle Ebook*

          979-8-88504-250-5 *Ebook*

*For the yellow ground and infinite blue sky
of the place that calls me home.*

Contents

Interlude

———

Between late 2019 and mid-2021, I was proud to be part of a farm business that was, in my view, visionary, transformative, and genuinely different. It was located about two hours from where I lived in Washington, DC, and I savored the few days each month that I got to spend there. I did a mix of things—sometimes I helped process chickens or provided an extra pair of hands for odd jobs, but mostly I was there to lend my skills in marketing, sales, planning, and strategy.

This work felt magical and important, and in 2020, when the pandemic made the future feel fraught with uncertainty, the farm seemed even more vital—to the world, our community, and me personally. This farm work was the most meaningful I had at the time, and the most fun, engaging, and impactful, even if it wasn't the easiest, most stable, or secure. I had worked for start-up companies before, including two that failed early, so I knew that this farm was still in its vulnerable beginnings and that any number of avoidable and unavoidable events could derail its progress. But I believed in this farm far more than I had believed in those other ventures, and I treasured my growing personal and professional relationships with the people who worked there.

Over the course of about a year, I immersed myself as much as I could in supporting the farm's work. What started as an occasional advisory visit and an agreement to create a new farmers market display evolved into helping manage online orders and participating in planning meetings. In mid-2020, the founder decided to raise funds, and the launch was wildly successful. Over the following months, we tried on many hats, pitched many ideas, and tried to professionalize. I interviewed accountants, vetted advisors, and supported the management of the founder's impossibly busy schedule. As the season came to a close, we planned for a significant expansion, and tried as often as we could to meet with the larger team to discuss and determine everyone's priorities, goals, and dreams.

The meetings were brutal. Much of the team was exhausted after long days of physical labor and disinterested in looking at spreadsheets and discussing plans for the relatively far and uncertain future. We struggled with distance and the limitations of pandemic precautions. We struggled with stark differences in communication styles and levels of comfort with varying worldviews and technologies. But more than anything, I think, we struggled because we had fundamentally different ideas of what we were trying to accomplish, and we didn't have enough time and energy to identify, understand, and work through those differences.

My role on the farm continued to shift. It wasn't until the beginning of 2021 that I had an official contract to work thirty hours per week, which turned out to be more a minimum than a maximum. By then, I was traveling to the farm every week to meet with the newly defined marketing team, which I ostensibly managed. We had daily virtual meetings with four to five people, and we were trying to hire collaboratively.

We were grinding to set up sales and marketing channels that could move tens of thousands of dollars of product a month, and an inventory and logistics system that could safely and efficiently do the same. We were simultaneously building the team's structure, writing our mission statement, defining and implementing our conflict resolution system, and doing our best to coordinate and work with other teams in a way that didn't add to their existing burdens. We were building the plane (or farm, as it were) as we were flying it.

But that iteration of the farm, operated by this group of people, did not make it. By April 2021, all but a couple of team members had been fired or quit in solidarity, including me. In the same week that I published my first book *Farm (and Other F Words)*, in which I deconstructed and argued against the small family farm model and elevated collective farming in a big team model instead, our own big team farm dissolved before our eyes. I felt utterly failed by the whole idea.

There are many reasons for what happened within this farm, and I know that every person involved has a unique perspective and understanding of what occurred and why. I have only one piece of the puzzle, and even taking it out to examine it now, nearly a year later, is incredibly painful. It is a shard of broken dream—sharpened by betrayed trust, financial hardship, lost friends, threats of violence, and the attacks of an online mob. Because of that pain, and because the story of our experience at that farm is something I hold collectively with my former colleagues, I will speak infrequently about it in these pages and only to my personal experiences.

In the immediate aftermath, I wrote an open letter, feeling it was necessary to speak my truth and defend my colleagues in what was quickly becoming a vicious and libelous back-and-forth on social media between a celebrity business owner and his former employees. At the time, I didn't know if this was the right thing to do, and to this day I get regular feedback from those who think it was not. All I can say is that I listened to my conscience and made the best choice available to me at the time.

Back then, I wrote about what had happened. I wrote about the disagreements, the isolation many of us experienced, and the disconnect between the public perception of our work and the reality on the ground. I wrote about why I stayed, about my responsibilities, and about my failure to see red flags that I had written explicitly about and warned against. Fearful that our experience would be held up as evidence that change was impossible, I wrote about my continued confidence in a more democratic food and farming system and my ongoing passion for supporting and building both.

After months of harassment and hate that followed our departure from the farm and my public letter, the prospect of writing a glowing treatise on big team farms seemed hopeless. How could I write a book extolling the benefits, tenets, and ways to support an idea that had, I felt, failed in practice, hurting so many people I cared about? Or worse, what if it wasn't that the idea had failed, but that I had somehow failed the idea? Perhaps it could've worked if it hadn't been for me—my whiteness, my background, my impatience. Though I was never the leader of this farm, nor even a full-time employee, I felt responsible for what had and hadn't happened. I felt like the kind of agricultural fraud who espouses an idea without ever successfully implementing it. I didn't think I'd be able to write this book, and for a long time, I didn't.

* * *

You've probably noticed that you are, in fact, reading a book. It's here in no small part because I said it would be. I promised this community, who honored me with their support, a book about big team farms. Whether it is the book that was hoped for is another matter entirely.

The commitment I made was to explore the concept of big team farms in detail, understand how they work in practice, and outline what policymakers, investors, farmers, and the public can do to support these organizations. You should know, when I was writing *Farm (and Other F Words)* I was at the peak of my confidence, which is, I think, where a person needs to be to challenge the status quo of a centuries-old system to its very core. Now, I am squarely in the valley of doubt. Even from my most optimistic vantage point, I see the big team farm idea as very, very hard to achieve.

My experience has shown me that a successful big team farm requires, at a minimum: outstanding communication skills, a deep commitment to shared goals, transparent and rigorous training, a healthy internal culture that encourages accountability and continuous personal growth, and well-established and articulated structures for conflict-resolution that can be accessed and reinforced by every member of the group. Collective systems require collective power and an incredible amount of humility and patience, especially from those in leadership roles. In essence, the model requires exceptional and ongoing personal and interpersonal work from every person involved in its creation and realization.

These basic requirements are only what is essential *internally* for a big team farm to succeed. There are external factors to face as well, many of which may well be impossible to overcome without millions of dollars in the bank. On top of the work of building these internal systems and surviving the battering of external forces, layer in the day-to-day physical, emotional, and financial strains of farming. Thriving through all of this is what the big team farm must aim to do.

In other words, if what you're expecting here is story after story about idyllic employee-owned and democratically-controlled farms and food businesses, well on their way to reshaping the system, you'll be sorely disappointed.

I often joke, when I talk to researchers, students, and reporters about problems in farming, that no matter how simple or straightforward a "why" question in American agriculture might seem, deep down, the answer is always capitalism.

A brief example: There's a recurring toxic algal bloom in the Gulf of Mexico that creates a "dead zone" of deoxygenated water that stretches for thousands of square miles in which marine life cannot survive (US EPA, 2022). Why is there a "dead zone"? Primarily because of nutrient runoff from Midwestern agricultural fields (Sauer, 2003). Why is there so much runoff? Because of the high concentration of farms and animal feeding operations in the Mississippi basin that improperly use or dispose of their fertilizer and animal waste (Berke, 2018). Why don't they properly use fertilizer or dispose of waste? Because it's "cheaper" not to, and no one is making them (Merchant, 2018), because American capitalism privatizes profit while externalizing many costs.

Responding to any agricultural question with a clipped "capitalism" is always good for a chuckle, but it's also usually true. America's brand of capitalism, with its complete lack of referees to correct market failures, allows all the advantages to flow towards the already-wealthy to the detriment of the public good. This system is in direct conflict with a big team farm future. Because of this, many who value the features of big team farms—which prioritize good jobs, good food, and good environmental outcomes—have found that in practice they've only been able to implement partial measures. Others have gone further towards these goals and retreated, finding that the social headwinds, the economic ones, or both, are simply too strong to overcome.

I would have loved for this book to offer an in-depth plan for an alternative to capitalism, in agriculture and beyond. But, for many reasons, it does not. I lack the expertise and the futuristic vision. And, more than anything, I believe that change has to be focused and clear for it to occur and stick, and it rarely involves changing everything at once. And capitalism, without doubt, touches every part of modern American life. This is not to say that this vision doesn't exist, it does, and I will defer to others to elucidate it.

For this book, however, I assume that when we start building big team farms, it will be under a regime of American capitalism. In part because I think a plan for change must start simultaneously at the point we want to reach and at the point where we are, and is achieved when those two ends meet. Given my experience, expertise, and research, I am best suited to start where we are. So I've stuck to looking closely at shorter term actions that people and organizations are already taking, with a view towards a longer-term strategy that is still unclear to me but which I know arches towards the good food, good jobs, and good environmental outcomes that we need.

Within these pages are stories of farmers and entrepreneurs trying to do something different. Some experts will be familiar to those who read *Farm (and Other F Words)*; others are fresh faces. None of them are taking on all the problems of the food and farming system in one go. Still, they're all tackling at least one aspect of selling good food, creating good jobs, and delivering good environmental outcomes, and they're doing it in unconventional ways—in general, ones that put the needs of many above the preferences of few.

There is a wide spectrum of possibilities between the extremes of the ruggedly individual small family farm and the collective big team farm. Along this continuum, people will find ways to organize their food and farm businesses that are tailored to the conditions of their community, geography, climate, crop, or market. An Indigenous farmer and faith leader, Randy Woodley, once told me that "all dichotomies are false." As we wade into these stories, keep this wisdom in mind. As we examine what these operators are doing, they usually won't fit neatly into either of these two categories. None of them are exclusively small family farms, nor big team farms. They're all somewhere in-between.

I have not found a conclusive answer as to whether it's possible to build a true big team farm. But Randy's wisdom reminds me that attaining an ideal is not the point. By necessity, an ideal is a two-dimensional thing. Like a painted portrait beside a real living, breathing human being, an ideal may be beautiful and masterful in perpetuity, as opposed to its living, aging, decaying counterpart, but the real thing is far more valuable. So, instead of worrying about the ideal, we'll explore farms that are trying to live the big team farm values as best they can and show you how it's going, warts and all.

For better or worse, I have shed the rose-colored glasses that I wore in the conclusion of my previous book as I described the possibilities of big team farms and how they could be a powerful force in shaping the future of the food and farm system. In part because I have been harshly corrected by my own experience. But beyond that, too, in my search for farms to feature in this book I found that many seemed to be doing it all, only to look under the hood and find an all too familiar dysfunction or aimlessness that I know leaves a business vulnerable. And the thing is, many businesses manage to hold on to that precarious footing right on into the peak of their success. But until we see that success, I think it only prudent to acknowledge the full story.

The good news for those looking for other perspectives on big team farm-type ideas is that there are so many leaders, farmers, and communicators out there creating resources to inspire you. Collective action and organization, especially in agriculture, is work that runs counter to much of white American culture, of which I am undeniably a part. Personally, I found interrogating the small family farm system much easier than exploring the full expression of big team farms, which I'm still learning to understand.

Moving forward together will take many people, much determined collaboration, a tremendous diversity of ideas, and, most importantly, time. Consider that the European plantation system of agricultural land occupation, the ancestor of the US farm system, has been in practice for almost five hundred years (Duff, 1992). It may well take generations for it to be undone.

It is intensely humbling and, for me, paradoxically hopeful to reckon with the scale of the challenge ahead. It means that no one will have all the answers, and no one experience is definitive, not even my own. So as we seek direction towards a radically transformed food and farming system, I hope this book stands as just a single note in a vast chorus of voices. As much as it serves as a resource in itself, I hope the people, resources, and suggestions for further reading found within these pages also make this book a gateway to a much wider universe of possibilities and ideas. Further, I hope that through the experiences of the farm and food workers you're about to meet you find tools that help you see yourself as part of a radically different system. I'm still learning how to see the unprecedented future—but others already have a hold of that vision.

Come on, I'll introduce you.

PART 1

GET IT THE FARM TOGETHER

BIG TEAM FARM PRINCIPLES

CHAPTER 1

Whose Farm?

Humble Hands Harvest farm is located at the top of a hill outside of Decorah, Iowa. This is the Driftless region in the Northeast of the state, a landscape full of big, rolling hills so unlike the pan-flat cornfields of stereotypical Iowa. This geography creates reality-bending microclimates, so when I drove up and out of Decorah's hot summer and into the hills, a cool breeze was already blowing in an early fall.

I met Hannah, one of the owners, for the first time in person on the twenty-two-acre diversified operation she started a few years back. We exchanged greetings outside a couple of greenhouses and a three-walled packing shed, littered with the detritus of countless weekly harvests, years of farmers markets, and the odd on-farm event. Then Hannah led me out to the farm proper, to introduce me to an expanse of late-season vegetable crops.

The planted beds, distant pastures for livestock, and ad hoc infrastructure are not unusual for a small-scale, first-generation farm. But right there in the middle of all the action was something quite unusual. A two-story house was starting to emerge from the hillside. This house was being built for the farmers—and not just Hannah, but for her current and future business partners and employees too.

It's not uncommon for farmers to provide housing as part of their compensation to farmworkers, but this house is not the traditional, seasonal dwelling for temporary laborers, nor is it Hannah's private residence. Hannah and her team's vision for Humble Hands is to create a space and a residence for a group of co-owners who work at and operate the farm as a collective.

This idea got its start in 2016 when, after a few years of farming solo, Hannah hit a wall with both her land tenure and farm work situation. She couldn't afford to rent the land and do all the work the way she wanted to do it by herself. So when Emily, an experienced farmer herself and Hannah's distant cousin, moved to town, Hannah asked if they could join forces.

"Our first year," Hannah told me by phone, "we just did a very simple buy-in of $1,000." The money went into a bank account owned by their newly formed LLC. "After that first year, we decided we needed to have something a little bit more intentional, when [Emily] knew for sure she wanted to stay. That's when we kind of dove in."

First, they needed to deal with the different levels of initial contribution, since Hannah had been operating the farm for four years before the two started collaborating. So they decided to set up as a worker-owned co-op with the help of community experts and resources from the Sustainable Economies Law Center. They rewrote their bylaws and the operating agreement of their LLC, and agreed to a buy-in price of $5,500, which both had already contributed. Today they each own half of the business and its assets, including the farmland Humble Hands owns, and they're looking forward to onboarding new worker-owners in the coming years.

This unusual farm ownership structure paired well with their unusual land tenure situation. The farm emerged on this particular hilltop because the adjacent community members were concerned, when these twenty-two acres went up for sale, that an industrial hog operation would be built that would ruin the land and the community. So neighbors organized to purchase the land in shares. They've been working with Humble Hands Harvest ever since, selling the farm their land-shares at cost to ensure that the land transitions to community-focused farming maintained by thoughtful stewards. So far, Hannah, Emily, and Humble Hands have been able to buy the majority of the twenty-two acres and to rent the remaining land.

Five seasons in, Hannah and Emily are focused on making sure the farm is a good place to work and own and on figuring out how to bring in new owners in a sustainable and fair way. Of the benefits of working with a partner-owner, Hannah says, "It's been really successful working with another person, because we have skills that complement each other. And we can talk each other down." Having a co-owner has also been valuable in terms of accountability and helping make both of their jobs a bit more sustainable. Plus, it's given them the space to be able to explore other opportunities, like creative partnerships within their local food system.

Farm ownership inspires powerful feelings, whether you're speaking with the heir to a multigenerational farm, a passionate agricultural upstart, or even a casual farmers market shopper. These emotions run the gamut, from gratitude for the farmer's salt-of-the-earth patriotism and our love of agrarian authenticity all the way to the vague but deeply held sense that farmers are just universally "good, hardworking people," and thus innately worthy. Many of these feelings arise from the fact that farm business ownership is inevitably tied up in the question of farm*land* ownership. And, in the US today, maintaining ownership over inherited land is often seen as a moral act more than a fiscal one.

Amid these intense emotions, a clear distinction is lost. As Duke University historian Gabriel Rosenberg pointed out in a recent essay, farmers are capitalists (2020). Though we think of farmers as "workers" of the land, in the modern US context, essentially all long-lasting farms rely first and foremost on their access to owned land. Therefore, "their economic interests are formed around the ownership of capital, which they use to extract surplus value from the labor of their employees." Private property rights in America are paramount, and people who lay claim to land, capital, or, increasingly, information and ideas, have the most power. Most American farmers are not workers, then, in the sense that they must exchange their labor for money to survive. Their land and capital holdings mean they can extract income through rents and asset appreciation, rather than depending on their own labor. This, perhaps surprising, is much closer to the original definition of the word farm—which meant to rent out, rather than to do the work of tending land (Merriam-Webster, 2022).

These realities are essential to keep in mind as we begin to think about farm ownership differently.

ON THE SACREDNESS OF LAND

Land is a sacred thing. It is home. It is where we begin life and end it, and, for a dwindling few, where we get to spend it. A homeland is a place with a niche into which we fit snuggly, where we belong, biologically and spiritually. We are quite literally made of the places we are from—we live and grow in cycles with the soil, minerals, microbes, plants, animals, and, critically, people that share our geography. The more work I do in agriculture, and the older I get, the more I am convinced that land is not a thing like other things. It is alive, and it lives in us in ways we don't really understand.

This is the nature of land we have to grapple with if we hope to build a better food system, and thus better farm businesses. If we could start from scratch, we would first define our overall economic systems to respect the true importance of land to us all. But our current economic system does not acknowledge these "nonmarket" qualities of land. Instead, our system revolves around individual rights to have and keep property, which reduces land to standardized, sterile units, so that any given acre can be identified, compared, bought and sold, used, and reused for whatever earns its current owner the highest returns.

I don't know that we can make meaningful progress towards a more just food and farm system while this atrophied idea of land ownership is still in place. We need to dismantle the systems—legal, social, and economic—that redistributed massive amounts of land and wealth almost exclusively to white families and individuals and continues to protect those holdings today. The question is how do we get from our current system to this dismantlement, given that we don't get to start from scratch?

From those within and around agriculture, I believe it requires continued criticism of the logic of private property ownership, farmland accumulation as a financial investment, and the social and political privilege granted to multigenerational landowners, which is directly tied to the US's imperial agrarian legacy. It will also require that alternative land use models, including commons and collective ownership, be taken seriously, not just by farmers and those within agriculture, but by the people who love, admire, and aspire to be farmers too.

There are extraordinary pressures in the US today being placed on those who are interested in starting farm and food businesses. Land is, essentially, inaccessible to all but the wealthiest Americans. The "bootstrap" strategy that worked for some in previous generations is no longer a viable way to begin farming. This reality, I think, offers a valuable opening to have a new conversation about how people get access to and own land, which could be a first step towards thinking fundamentally differently about our relationship to our sacred landscapes.

A REAL, ACTUAL FARM SHARE

In the big team farm world, farm ownership is transformed from the be-all-end-all of individual destiny into a meaning-infused tool that can be used to attract and motivate a diverse team who will grow and secure the business.

This transformation begins with the nature of a farm business itself. In most cases, the value of a farm business is the sum total of its resources and opportunities. Resources include the equipment, stock, and other physical property, and may include the farmland if it's owned or a rental relationship and agreement. A farm business's opportunities are more nebulous, including factors like its brand and customer accounts, as well as business strategy, plans, and networks.

Especially in the early stages of a farm, the need to invest in the farm business is often significant and creates a difficult trade-off between time and money. When an independent farmer is juggling a necessary tractor replacement, cultivating customers, and expansion plans, all while taking care of day-to-day operations, for example, it is challenging to find more than the bare minimum in terms of time and cash to invest in recruiting and retaining workers. A bigger team, however, is often essential to take advantage of more opportunities. Many farmers feel like they can't pay enough workers, nor can they pay their workers enough, and also cover the farm's expenses. This often leaves farms understaffed and with under-compensated and unmotivated employees—adding new management duties to leaders often without taking much but the most basic work off their plate. And, for many farmers, that "most basic work" is often the work they like the most.

According to Lance Woodbury, a farm business advisor, his most progressive clients are thinking about this trade-off, between investing resources in the business and investing in employees, fundamentally differently. They're leveraging what they do have—namely, ownership—to attract and keep talent that they otherwise couldn't afford.

Depending on what resources are available and what kind of talent the team needs, Lance says there are a lot of ways for farm businesses to be creative with ownership. Some of his clients have explored having key employees earn a share of the business annually as part of their compensation, having the opportunity to purchase stakes over time or, in one extraordinary case, offering to contribute $350,000 towards a house for employees who remain at the farm for twenty years. Especially for young farmworkers, who are looking for the opportunity not only to work in agriculture but also to find a path to ownership, these offers are potent enticements. And there are big benefits for existing farmers, too, who can leverage this kind of sharing to transition out of farming at a pace that's right for them, knowing that the land they treasure will still be cared for. "The farms that have those conversations," Lance says, "tend to get ahead."

When I describe this strategy to farmers, without fail, the first question is always some variation on: "How will that impact my ability to pass this farm onto my children?"

I had a conversation with a farmer in this exact situation, who was running a struggling farm business on land they owned. I challenged them about why they were so concerned with ensuring that their very young children would be able to inherit a failing business in two decades (the land was not inherited). Mumbles and grumbles followed, to the tune of, "They grew up here, they've helped, they deserve to own it if they want." I asked whether their infant children have contributed more than the adult farm employees, and, if pouring love and labor into a business makes a person more deserving of ownership, why should their children be first in line? Might the employees also be able to make the farm more successful when empowered through part-ownership, and, through that process, free up enough time for the farmer to actually watch those children grow up?

That farmer didn't want to hear these questions, but if you're currently an independent owner of a farm business I hope you'll take some time to consider them. Employee ownership, for this farm and likely for many others, is simultaneously an investment in the owner and their family, in the longevity of the business, and in the employees themselves.

Sharing ownership also does *not* erase the opportunity for descendants to join the farm business one day. First, the original owner is likely to keep an ownership stake, which can be sold or willed to heirs. And second, if the farm's co-owners set up a system that allows new partners to buy in as the need and opportunity arises, children and other relatives could always buy in when they're ready, as junior partners, if their skills and goals align with what the business actually needs.

During difficult times on the farm, co-ownership allows owners to share in one of the most reliable sources of financial gain within farm businesses—increasing land value—without selling the land. For example, though co-owners like Hannah and Emily may struggle to pay themselves what most would consider a livable wage in the short-term, they will share in the longer-term benefits of the increased land value, and thus accrue returns to their labor.

Partner- (or even employee-) owned farm and food businesses are already succeeding in the agricultural sector, especially where high-value labor can add a lot to the bottom line. Dairies and other livestock farms, in particular, have taken to this model of ownership, as they find that the likes of animal nutritionists, veterinarians, or other specialists need more than the promise of an hourly wage to consider farm work a competitive job offer. It's notable that outside the farm sector it's common to compensate critical employees with ownership stakes, or equity, in the business. Interested farmers can look to examples in the worlds of start-up companies, law firms, and manufacturing to find tried and true shared ownership models.

Another significant benefit of ownership-sharing is its potential to bring more lucrative opportunities to rural areas. The isolation and loneliness of farming discourages many farm-curious people from pursuing or sticking with agriculture, and finding a way to fulfill that need for connection in rural communities is vital. This need motivated Nebraska commodity grain farmer Clay Govier to rethink how ownership can be leveraged on his farm, although he struggled with communicating these shifting priorities across generations.

"My dad obviously values ownership," Clay says, "and I think that's a generational thing. Like, it's his biggest thing. It's not even about making a bunch of money every year. It's more about owning the ground and maintaining ownership." But from Clay's perspective this obsession with ownership is a handicap when thinking about finding and retaining employees. He's considering creative alternative models instead—like profit-sharing, paying off an employee's student loans, or offering equity. In Clay's mind, it's about finding the right set of incentives to attract and keep the employee or partner the farm business needs, not about finding a standard package that works for a generic person.

"Most farmers just think, 'Well, I guess I'll just have to pay them more.' But I think that doesn't understand the values of who you're trying to hire. Understanding the value system of individuals is super tricky, but I think that's going to be the biggest piece of the puzzle for diversifying operations, finding that labor, and growing these rural communities." Today the farm's only current nonowner employee is a local University of Nebraska grad who wanted to move back to town and raise cattle. Clay's farm helps support his small herd with grazing land.

By de-prioritizing individual or family farm ownership, shared ownership is a tremendous opportunity, particularly for farms that already own land. Once a farmer can mentally detach the farm business from their family, and therefore farmland and assets from their personal wealth, it makes it easier to understand that the point of farming is not to hold on to the land at all costs; but to make a profit and run the business well—and for that good people are essential. Plus, it offers a way for farmers to keep employees even during bad years, since ownership of an asset that appreciates (like farmland) allows co-owners to gain and grow wealth, even if their take-home pay is low.

Ownership can also be outright sold to employees as a group, which is a niche exit strategy popular among retiring business owners who want to ensure that their employees won't lose their jobs and their communities won't lose a key source of economic activity (Sullivan, 2020). There are meaningful tax benefits to this strategy, both for the original business owners and the employees. This strategy has proven to make organizations more resilient and, in many instances, more successful. In most cases the most significant trade-off is that selling a business to employees, usually through an employee stock ownership plan (ESOP) or other existing model, doesn't net the kind of jaw-dropping payout the owners might get from an investment firm. Employees are limited by law from paying more than fair market value for their shares. However, with more than six thousand businesses bought out through ESOPs active in the US today, including several farms and food businesses, many owners and employees alike have found this a meaningful way to create a more long-lasting and democratic workplace.

A final note on sharing ownership: for many beginner farmers, the problem is that buying farmland or owning assets like buildings, livestock, and equipment is still a ways off. Many farmers, when they're just starting out, are renting land, finding cheap, used equipment, and creating markets for their products from the ground up. Farms in their earliest stages can also pursue employee ownership or partnership, but it requires some forethought about how ownership will be determined, how contributions and expenses will be divvied up, and what roles each participant will fulfill.

SHARING DECISIONS

The task of ultimate decision-making in traditional, hierarchical business structures rests squarely on the shoulders of the owners and their deputies. Most of us are familiar with the benefits of this system, with its efficiencies, accountability, and clear lines of authority. Nonetheless, the trade-offs are steep, especially in high-stress environments like farming where the diversity of problems and responsibilities often threatens to overwhelm the one or two people at the top.

A key weakness in businesses where all the decision-making power is held by one or few related people is a lack of innovative thinking. Even the most brilliant operators need advisors and supporters, especially when a person has to transition throughout a day between being a visionary, a salesperson, an accountant, a landscape planner, a mechanic, and more, as a farmer is wont to do. A lack of exposure to outside input and fresh perspectives in critical decision-making makes it difficult to find novel solutions, move quickly on—or even identify—new opportunities, and stay ahead of competition.

Farm entrepreneurs who are responsible for all planning and decision-making are not only likely to struggle with innovation, but are also intensely susceptible to burnout. The psychological pressure of making dozens or hundreds of decisions a day, that not only affect themselves and their coworkers but also animals, land, ecosystems, and whole communities, can be devastating, especially when compounded with financial strain and general uncertainty.

One of the inherent difficulties in making decisions about land use is that it's impossible for one person to consider all the different factors, effects, and possible implications of a decision in a complex environment. An individual is inevitably limited by their own biases, weaknesses, and blind spots, and without collaborators around to offer diverging perspectives, to advocate for alternatives, and to consider overlooked details, mistakes are much more likely to occur.

Prioritizing diversity among co-owners and employees is a useful antidote to these problems. Substantive research in recent years has shown that more diverse teams lead to improved decision-making and more insights and innovation. Working within more diverse teams also increases motivation and job satisfaction (McKinsey, 2020). Diversifying ownership diversifies the business, creating a radical kind of stability that empowers every employee and partner with the fight and drive of a farmer protecting the homestead, because that is what they are.

Hierarchical decision-making amongst owners is not an essential part of running any kind of business, especially a farm. Hannah and Emily's story at Humble Hands Harvest offers a clear alternative. The farm was organized into a worker-owned collective in 2018, and it's visioning documents call "for democratic ownership and decision-making, allows room for growth, enables access to farmers with limited capital, [and] has an exit strategy." We'll discuss more possible structures in the next chapter.

Ownership not only creates an opportunity to fan an employee's entrepreneurial flame but it can also increase accountability and alter the way employees think about decision-making, time horizons, and their vision for their careers. Ari Weinzweig, in his 2010 book *A Lapsed Anarchist's*

Approach to Building a Great Business, discusses why the business he cofounded, Zingerman's, has grown from the single deli in Ann Arbor, Michigan, into a vast community of owner-operated businesses. Zingerman's leaders chose to utilize new partners for expansion instead of hiring managers, in part because they believe that on-site owner-operators bring "energy, excitement, [and] commitment to food, service and staff" that managers and absentee-owners don't. This strategy also keeps "decision-making where it belongs—close to the customer and close to the food." This wisdom is meaningful for farms, too, because it applies not only in the field but also in front of customers, investors, and other supporters. Owners act differently than employees; that's all there is to it.

None of this is to say that having co-owners or additional partners is a panacea. The folks at Zingerman's, for example, certainly have their share of issues and imperfections, just like every other business. The difference is the way the team deals with those problems, in their own words, "in a positive, performance-oriented, values-driven, mission-focused, caring, and giving way" (Weinzweig, 2010).

Naturally, not every employee will want to be an owner. Some who choose to work in agriculture do so because of a desire to be mobile, spontaneous, and to experience a variety of lives and work. Some will not be intrigued by ownership because of the cost, the potential burdens, or simply because they don't feel they (or you) have the necessary skills or experience to make it work. That's fine. Not every employee has to be an owner. Ownership can be a complex, legalistic, and nuanced thing. Though "part-owning a farm" might sound good to many on its face, any potential partner or co-owner must understand all the rights, responsibilities, and commitments that come with the benefits of being an owner, which will likely require an investment in training or education on the part of the founder.

It's worth reiterating that even if your farm business doesn't own farmland, that doesn't mean the business has nothing that could appeal to would-be partners. Farm businesses often have plenty of other valuable assets. A well-known brand, a sizable customer base, good relationships with key stakeholders, even good pricing analysis and business plans are all pieces of intellectual property that give your farm business value. Putting a dollar figure on these assets can be difficult, but knowing the value of your business's tangible and intangible assets is vital to understanding the farm's overall financial health.

Diversifying ownership is a powerful way to recognize that a single farmer is unlikely to have all the technical skills of farming, the management skills to coordinate day-to-day operations, and the revolutionary vision that can lead a farm through the next century of unprecedented change. If a farmer doesn't want to be responsible for managing a team, that's fine, they can bring on a partner to fill the management gap. If a visionary entrepreneur doesn't want to do the farming day-to-day, that's fine too, they can bring on a technical founder to build that strategy and motivate the team. This kind of organization may feel foreign in farming, but it's a well-trodden path in other business sectors that farmers are welcome to use.

THE WHY OF FARM OWNERSHIP

The ideas of nonfamily partnerships and employee-ownership may make farmers and nonfarmers alike squirm. But these strategies offer one of the most direct routes to the changes we want to see in farming. These models could get us to a place that prioritizes creating more opportunities on the land for new farmers and ensure more voices get to participate in deciding how land is used.

The benefits of rethinking independent farm business ownership accrue all throughout the system. Broadening farm ownership can take the strain of being solely responsible for an impossible amount of decision-making off the shoulders of individual farmers. At the same time, it grants a more diverse group of people the power to farm in a way that's true to them. Prioritizing shared farm ownership creates a real possibility for historically marginalized groups to gain access to land, and the wealth that owning it often builds. And by creating opportunities for more farmers from all backgrounds to become farm *owners*, not by buying private farmland but by working with others who are similarly aligned, we also make it more likely that a given community can access the food they want and need.

Overall, more diverse farm-owning teams will create a considerably more resilient farm system than the one we have today. These teams will be better positioned to prepare for cataclysmic events, predict challenges and create plans to overcome them, and deal with the unpredictable when it arises.

Distributing ownership gives businesses access to more people, perspectives, and opportunities—more eyes and brains, making it more likely that problems will be spotted and avoided. In the toughest moments, when a farm business might be in peril, distributed ownership also means a wider possible support network and more people motivated to put the health of the organization over their individual wants. And in the long-term, farm businesses that foster a diverse group of owners and leaders are less likely to collapse after the departure of a founder, which in turn relieves the pressure on individuals to continue no matter what.

There are always trade-offs, of course. When a farm has more than one owner, the traditional, familiar, and comfortable work hierarchies will likely be challenged. In many cases, owners must make decisions jointly, introducing the complications of different personalities, biases, and communication styles. But Lance Woodbury says these limitations can be mitigated with proper due diligence.

"A key to any of this is figuring out how to get out of business before you get into business together. Part and parcel with that conversation is, what if it doesn't work out? Or what if the person leaves early or things like that," he says. He's helped farm owners craft shareholder or operating agreements that allow for disputes, for other opportunities arising that might pull owners away, and how the business will manage through these challenges. The ideal agreement is unique to every situation, he explains, but it should involve careful consideration by all involved, alignment on long-term goals, and it should be legally binding. For every farm business, determining and building structures, policies, and procedures will be mentally and emotionally taxing and time-consuming work. It will almost certainly require the support of a lawyer or another kind of cooperative/employee-ownership expert to ensure the legality and enforceability of the agreement.

All this effort is well worth it, Lance says, because for an individual farm owner the question is not whether or not they will get out of farming one day—because everyone will. The real question is, "How [do] we get out of business, and do that collaboratively in a way that lets the individuals or family go on and be successful in other endeavors [...] while maintaining good relationships?" Being able to answer this question, he says, is the sign of success, whereas hanging on to the family land at any cost, even when it damages bodies, relationships, and livelihoods, is not.

NO ONE FARMS ALONE

Many of our most intransigent problems in agriculture today cannot be solved by perpetuating the one family, one farm model. Consider the radical racial and gender inequality in our current farm system, or the near complete lack of access to farmland and other resources for beginning farmers and ranchers. Consider problems of farm consolidation, of the "hollowing out" of rural America. The economic realities of our current small family farm-centric system do not offer an off-ramp from this collateral damage.

Randy Woodley, the Indigenous farmer we met in the interlude, explained the role of individualism, and bias against the collective, as it is ingrained in American agriculture and its small family farm mythology. This bias is fundamental, he says, to the Western worldview, which is strictly attached to dualism. This dualism breaks things—animals, people, ideas, everything—into binaries and then necessitates comparison. This worldview splits "individuals" from "groups" and demands we decide which is better and more important. In general, we choose individuals.

"Which is neurosis," Randy says, "it's neurotic. We weren't made to live as individual people. But it's part of that whole American dream of 'you got to have this for you and yours,' and someone else getting that gives a new someone the impetus to do that for themselves. And everybody's competing with each other to try and get their little place in space, rather than saying, 'Let's share and be a part of a community.'" This thinking pervades every part of our lives. Much of Randy's work, in agriculture and beyond, has aimed not just to decenter individualism but to challenge the whole idea of dualism.

"We do ceremonies out here," Randy says, describing how he does this work on his own farm, from farm work, religion and community, to rest and celebration. "But this is all connected, right? In the Western world, it's all segregated. It's like, this is about growing stuff. And this is about business. And everybody puts in so many hours. But life just doesn't work that way."

This idea is important to keep in mind when thinking about building collective ownership. It's difficult and messy, and sharing power, responsibilities, and hardships will not be a cut and dry process. In most cases, it involves something like a marriage—a long-term commitment to shared goals and priorities. It requires that we care more about working together than having all the power. Undoubtedly, the nature of these relationships will change over time as each of the people involved grow and evolve. Collective ownership requires trust, good-faith participation, and a certain amount of comfort with discomfort. But—if one of the things we care about most is building and maintaining systems and communities that outlive us—the benefits of collective ownership far outweigh the costs. This work inevitably requires a reckoning with human fallibility and mortality, and it offers a pathway for us to understand what it means to be part of something bigger than ourselves.

At Humble Hands, even with Emily now in the mix, there's still a ton of work to be done; between managing the perennial crops (like apples), the seasonal vegetables, the livestock, the markets, and participating in community food work, there's definitely enough work for more hands.

"So that means that we are trying to figure out how to bring on more people in a way that meshes with our style," Hannah says. "We really like working with other people, but we don't like managing them. So we have an employee right now, and we've decided on a three-year trajectory toward ownership of the business. But it's not totally clear if she will continue that trajectory or not."

The question of managing and growing employees, beyond how to afford them, is a tricky problem for many farm owners to solve. But I'd argue that great farmers grow people more than any other crop.

CHAPTER 2

Grow a People-System

———

Regenerative agriculture emphasizes diversity: of plants and animals, of soil biota, even of tools and resources. But far too often, the system's emphasis on diversity ends right before it gets to the people involved.

Why is that? In part, I think, it's because families—the idealized workers of farms—are, by definition, low on diversity. Genetic relatives who live and grow together tend to be relatively similar, likely to have similar ideas and mind-sets and to find similar solutions to problems. And when they don't—when family members in a farm setting aren't on the same page—the outcomes are often catastrophic: divorces, estrangements, and general breakups that often devastate the business while inflicting deep emotional wounds that can persist for generations.

Beyond the simple fact that families tend to be low in tangible diversity, families also tend to be, in modern times, low on sheer numbers. Only the rarest family would be big enough to even attempt to invest in the expertise needed to fill the positions required on a modern farm, and even rarer still is the family that could do so *and* function as a highly effective team.

The fact is ecosystems need diversity, and their need for diversity doesn't stop at the human level.

That's why in a big team farm world, farmers are, more than anything, tenders of people. Farmers are coordinators of teams, builders of skills, soothers of social and emotional wounds, and maintainers of peace. In agriculture as much as any other sector, people are a farm's most important asset.

Sharing ownership is a critical way of creating a more diverse, and often more democratic, farm business, but it is not the only way. Owning the business itself is only part of the equation—another part is ownership over the business's goals, community, and over your own individual work. Many farms I've learned from have found that prioritizing this internal empowerment is nothing short of transformative.

The first and most important responsibility of farm business's leaders is maintaining the symbiosis between culture and systems. And all of this necessarily begins by reckoning with the nature of farm work itself.

ON THE SACREDNESS OF PEOPLE

People are sacred beings. People are our family, friends, ancestors, acquaintances, heroes, nemeses, and descendants. We, as people, share a fundamental craving to know ourselves and to be known by one another, to walk in life with the people we love and bear witness to their joy and pain, their triumphs and disasters, and to have the freedom to be who we are. Being people and being able to live with dignity in ways that respect and aim to honor our complex hopes, loves, fears, and desires is, I think, the whole point of what we're doing here.

This is an incomplete description of the nature of people, of which work is just one of many elements. This is what we have to grapple with if we hope to build a better food system, and thus better farm businesses. If we were aiming to create a system from scratch, we would first define our overall economic systems to respect the true significance we find in ourselves and one another—and only after that, in our work. But our current economic system does not acknowledge these "nonmarket" qualities of labor. Instead, our system reduces people to "human resources," rendering precious and fleeting human lifetimes into work hours that are supposedly interchangeable, and thus disposable. Especially in the food and farm system, workers have been abandoned by labor protections and left vulnerable to economic, social, and physical violence that traps them in the most dangerous jobs in the worst-paying sector of our economy.

I don't know that we can make meaningful progress towards a more just food and farm system while this despicable system of labor exploitation is in place. We need to dismantle the systems that have dehumanized, and then entrenched the exploitation of, those marginalized for generations as result of race, gender, and many other factors. But how do we move towards this dismantlement?

I believe that, from those within and around agriculture, it requires fighting against the logic of agricultural exceptionalism that exempts farmworkers from labor protections. It requires combatting the "poor farm" narrative and other excuses for why the agriculture and food sectors "can't afford" to protect and compensate farm and food workers fairly. It will also require alternative organizational models that democratize and empower workers to be seriously considered by farmers, the sector more broadly, and workers themselves.

There are extraordinary pressures being placed on those who are looking for farmworkers and for those who work, willingly or not, in agriculture. Farmworkers are becoming increasingly scarce, and greater skill and technological proficiency amongst employees is of growing importance (Rosenblatt, 2021). This reality, I think, offers a valuable opening to have a new conversation about how we think about and treat farm labor, which could be a first step towards thinking fundamentally differently about the value of people and the work they do on farms.

SHIFTING MINDSETS AROUND FARM WORK

The common wisdom in agriculture is that labor is the most expensive element of a farm business and, because food prices are low, farms must pay their workers as little as possible.

Patrick Robinette, the farmer-owner of Harris-Robinette Beef and Micro Summit Processors, disagrees.

"Our approach is that our employees are craftsmen," Patrick told me in a phone call from his home in North Carolina. "We're going to take our time and build craftsmanship."

Harris-Robinette doesn't sell commodity beef, Patrick tells me, because commodity beef simply doesn't pay. The truly enormous operations, like Tyson or Smithfield, capture too many efficiencies of scale for any smaller businesses to compete. In other words, the giants can afford to earn just a few cents per unit because they'll sell millions or billions of them. These multinationals focus on a bottom-line model that exploits labor and mechanization, leading to high output while making miserable, low-paying work for employees largely drawn from migrant and refugee populations. During the COVID-19 pandemic, thousands of these workers were sickened, and hundreds died from the virus they contracted at work (Douglas, 2021).

Micro Summit Processors, the regional meat processing facility that Patrick opened, isn't trying to play that game. He's found a different model, and it starts with the hiring and training process.

"The first thing is, I don't find anybody that has any prior knowledge about slaughter processing. In fact, my latest hire is a dude who has a degree in theater arts from the University of South Carolina." Patrick says a lack of experience is a boon because he doesn't want to fight against the habits employees might have picked up in other facilities. Instead, he focuses on a more fundamental attribute: people who care about themselves and their work.

He's created a hands-on training process; it gradually builds from learning the basics of how to hold a knife and move cattle around in the pen and progresses all the way to fine butchery skills. Everyone learns and becomes a well-rounded and highly skilled asset to the business. And it shows in employee turnover rates. Before new hires were brought on to help with the COVID-19 rush, neither the meatpacking operation nor the parallel farm Patrick runs needed to hire a new employee in years. In the plant, fourteen people crank out about forty thousand pounds of meat a week.

Patrick has felt the temptation to follow in the footsteps of bigger meatpackers, too. But when he was confronted with the seemingly imminent rise of robotics in meat processing, he consciously moved in the other direction. He's confident there's real value in human craftsmanship that will continue to earn a premium.

"When we went from independent processing to the Big Four [National Beef, JBS, Tyson, Cargill]," he says, "we also went from craftsmanship to boxed beef, and we devalued our animals." Robotics, he believes, will only further devalue meat because there is just too much variability in living animal bodies. Human brains and living hands best adapt to variations in muscle sizes, placements, attachments, and other biological idiosyncrasies. He sees too how celebrity chefs and cooking media have led a renaissance in butchery and believes that his customers will value human butchers more and more. In that way, he believes investing in skilling up his employees is a better bet than high-tech equipment.

Patrick's experience illustrates that people, more than any piece of equipment that necessarily depreciates with use, are an investment in the future of a farm's profitability. Labor doesn't have to be an expense to be minimized at all costs. High-quality, deeply engaged, well-matched people can be the biggest contributor to a farm's top line.

Another way to look at it, as a Southern California food business owner once told me: "I can't afford $15/hour salespeople, but I can't *not* afford to have $27 or $30/hour salespeople." Like any other kind of investment, the quality of labor is often proportional to its cost. The farm sector is obsessed with paying as little as possible, sometimes nothing at all, for farm work, but in reality, the added benefit of well-trained labor in farming can far outweigh the cost.

Underlying the general aversion in agriculture to paying farm employees well is the assumption that farming is unskilled work. The reality is that there is no such thing as unskilled work. All work requires some amount of training, talent, effort, and focus. The idea that the technical work of farming is inherently "low skill," somehow easy to acquire, or based only on physical ability has undoubtedly lured many people to unsuccessful farming careers. But most who have eventually picked up those skills will recognize that there's nothing "low skill" about the complex and dynamic work of procuring food from landscapes. It requires deep intimacy with specific geographies, organisms, and natural resources, a lot of experience with edge-cases, and a range of adaptable competencies.

Farming well, then, requires the people who work on farms (who are commonly denied the sacred label "farmer" for the less romantic "farmworker") to be full-time, long-term employees who can participate and be compensated appropriately.

WHEN IN DOUBT, CHOOSE DEMOCRACY

When figuring out the employee compensation for his processing plant workers, Patrick leaned into his mind-set shift and decided to go with a radical transparency model. He cracked open the business's books, took the time to train up his people on how the business works, and asked them to decide on a fair wage.

"We can put 30 percent of our revenue into the pot for labor," Patrick reports telling his workers. "So I said, 'Here's the pot. The more people you need me to hire to get that job done, the less the pot is. But it's up to you.'" His employees took it upon themselves to determine how many hours they wanted to work, and at what rate, to meet the business's production targets. This gave them meaningful control over the size of their team, the number of hours they worked, and the size of their paychecks.

"We're not here to break a sweat," is Patrick's motto. He tells me a story from his days working on a Montana ranch in high school that informed this outlook. The rancher asked him to fetch something from the shop, and Patrick shot off at a run to get it. But the rancher called him back after a few seconds, spitting mad. "He says, 'There's only two times in your life you should be running. The first is when something's on fire, and the second is when the husband's coming home.'" Patrick has taken that logic to heart and his management style reflects that insistence against overwork.

"When you're working above and beyond, that's when accidents happen, that's when things go wrong," he says. So, he's made a concerted effort to align incentives to make sure that his employees can work the number of hours they want for reasonable compensation, but that they also have mechanisms to get more help when they need it.

"We put the power to the employee; we treat them like they're part of the operation. You're not a commodity here." The business has even been able to go a step further, helping pay for employees' college education or for English lessons for nonnative speakers.

Patrick's example shows how transformative it is to recognize the dignity of the people in a farm business setting. And further, this organization shows how able people are to make the best decision for themselves *and* the business when given the opportunity. Patrick's workers didn't opt for the most self-serving option, but instead landed on a decision that was optimized for the specific individuals involved without putting the long-term viability of the business they work for in peril. At the core of this move towards a democratized workplace is the idea that when people are empowered and have the information they need, they're quite good at complex decision-making.

Another food and farming company in the US is even farther along this path to democratization, driven by a very similar realization. This company, Morning Star, has grown to be a national player in its specific niche: tomatoes.

I first met Doug in his small, cluttered home office in California's central valley. He was wearing a white button-down, looking every bit the corporate leader most comfortable in the boardroom, suddenly quarantined. I had asked for a meeting to talk about Morning Star Foods, a tomato processing company you've probably never heard of, though you've almost certainly tasted their product (barring a tomato allergy). The business made nearly a billion dollars in 2019, is the largest tomato processor in the world, and grows, processes, and distributes about 40 percent of all the tomato-paste-based foods in the US.

But this food and farm company isn't unusual just for its size. It's unusual because in its thirty-year history, it's never hired a single employee. Instead, during its peak season, Morning Star is staffed by twenty-four hundred entirely self-managed colleagues.

"The language that we use is important, and it helps define our culture," Doug says. "The language of HR is very dehumanizing. The term Human Resources itself is a dehumanizing term, and deliberately so." Doug points out that what were once personnel departments made the switch to HR in the 1980s to pave the way for a reengineering craze, where millions of people were laid off or made expendable.

"People aren't resources; they're human beings," he explains, "So, we talk about people. We talk about things that are important, things like purpose, meaning, and belonging; transcendent language that can actually serve to motivate people and inspire them to greatness. That's the reason we chose 'colleague.'" They choose it over other options too, Doug says, because it connotes a certain professional context, and at Morning Star everyone is considered a professional. "We've obliterated this artificial dichotomy between blue-collar and white-collar. We have no collar. We consider the janitors to be professionals. Everyone's a professional at Morning Star and is treated as such with the full dignity you'd expect."

The story of Morning Star's radical rethinking of tomato processing began in 1990, when founder Chris Rufer started to build his first processing factory. Doug had worked with Chris before at another tomato company, but they'd felt like something was missing, so Chris struck out on his own.

"We sort of defaulted to traditional organizational management, a pyramid structure. Our founder was at the top, and then we had a layer of managers, of which I was one, the financial controller. Then we have a layer of supervisors [...]. And then we had a layer of coordinators who carried out the wishes of the supervisors. And then we had everybody else who did the actual work at the bottom of the pyramid." But as time passed the problems of this command-and-control system started to weigh on everyone. The bureaucracy was distracting, disruptive, and frustrating in every direction.

One day, Doug recalls, Chris was watching people drive into the parking lot and go to their workstations. He realized that every single one of those people is already a manager in their own personal life. They're all making gigantic, life-altering decisions, on their own. They decide who to date and marry, what to do for a living, whether to buy a house, car, or to have kids—all without a boss. And so, for Chris that begged the question: If people know what to do and how to do it, then why do they need a boss at work?

So Chris got his then twenty-four employees together and handed out a document called the Morning Star Food Principles.

"This was his proposal for governance, and the principles boiled down to two things. The first principle was that people shouldn't use force against other people. And the second principle was that people should keep the commitments they make to each other, keep their promises." At the time, Doug says, the team just discussed and debated for a couple of hours. In the end, they decided to adopt the principles, and by the time they left the meeting they had become a self-managed organization.

"No human bosses, no managers, no supervisors, no vice presidents, no titles, no command authority of any kind." Doug says it felt quite radical even then. But by July of that year, they turned on the factory and produced ninety million pounds of tomato paste; changing the cost structure of the entire industry in the process and becoming a near-instant price leader. The organization has continued to grow, adding two more factories and expanding up and down the supply chain, from farming and tracking all the way through warehousing and logistics.

"We've never deviated from our two core principles: don't use force and keep commitments." Those outside the food sector have taken notice too. Morning Star made the cover of the *Harvard Business Review* as "The World's Most Creatively Managed Company" (Hamel, 2011).

In practice, these principles translate not into formal and static job descriptions but instead into a set of agreements that each colleague makes with their coworkers. Each colleague defines their own role and shares it with all the relevant colleagues they'll have to work with to accomplish their duties. The colleagues negotiate the distribution of tasks among themselves, and they create a formal agreement, which each interdependent colleague has the power to enforce.

"We call these agreements Colleague Letters of Understanding," Doug explains. A computer lab at the University of California, Davis created a visualization of the "org chart" at Morning Star. Instead of the classic pyramid, the organization is a dense, twisting spiderweb of interconnecting nodes, existing in three-dimensional space (Laloux, 2014). "And if it were a time-lapse movie, it would be in constant motion because people are free to renegotiate their roles and responsibilities. So we like to think [that this allows for] stronger, better teamwork and leadership than a traditional, top-down company." Doug says the organization has seen significant benefits in terms of increased creativity and employee happiness in addition to reduced bureaucracy. A critical part of that bias against bureaucracy extends all the way to traditionally touchy areas like purchasing. Any employee at Morning Star with a need, Doug says, has the ability to make a purchase themselves. In that way, power is meaningfully distributed.

Further, the thousands of colleagues during the peak summer season shrinks to about four hundred in the off-season, all without a single HR manager to coordinate who stays and who leaves. Those decisions are considered, negotiated, and finalized by individual members and teams throughout the organization. Hearing Doug describe their principles it certainly sounds peachy, but he notes that it isn't always easy.

"It's a challenging environment; it requires courage on the part of participants to speak up and challenge their fellow colleagues. There are no bosses walking around to reprimand people or pat them on the back for doing a good job. People have to tell themselves how they're doing with their own scorecards, and they have to hold their fellow colleagues accountable; they have to be able to deliver feedback, and those conversations aren't easy." Doug says that finding individuals with these social capacities and training colleagues in these methods is one of Morning Star's greatest challenges. Acculturating people who have had leadership roles in more hierarchical businesses is a particular challenge. People who have benefited from perks, promotions, titles, and command structures are usually loath to give them up and can have the most difficulty figuring out how to marshal and express the soft power that Morning Star thrives on. This power, as described in *Reinventing Organizations* by Frederic Laloux, is all about social skills: being able to negotiate with colleagues to get work done, identify opportunities, and extend your sphere of influence in the organization in a way that makes the whole team more effective (2011).

"Asking those people to enter into an ecosystem where everything is done by request and response, and there's zero command authority, it's a big ask. And some people profess to be willing to make the transition and find they can't." More junior people, who have less experience at the top of hierarchies, might seem likely to be more successful, but those people face their own challenges.

"There's no career ladder—people are completely responsible for managing their own careers, training, and development. The organization makes resources available and provides coaching and mentoring, and people are free to exercise their free will and take advantage of outside resources. So if you need that in your life, this is not the place for you to work." Doug says Morning Star ignores the "currency" of titles and instead gives colleagues an opportunity to grow and refine a portfolio of work. As the nature of labor more broadly continues to evolve, Doug believes, this will help Morning Star colleagues be more successful, within the organization or without.

This freedom to chart one's own path has led to some amazing outcomes. Doug describes a young mechanic at Morning Star's first factory that had an ambition to become an industrial electrician—a dangerous job that usually requires at least four years of highly technical learning alongside extensive on-the-job training. This mechanic needed a willing mentor who could take the time to teach him and work out a learning program to develop the necessary skills. Since colleagues have to take time out of meeting their own duties and developing their own skills to mentor one another, they're cautious about signing on. They insist on a reasonable forecast of success, taking into account aptitude, dedication, and potential.

"So this young man found a willing mentor, and they worked out a learning program that involved community college coursework, on-the-job training, learning articles, videos, podcasts, books, and practice simulations." At the end of this four year long, customized course, the mechanic became an industrial electrician. "Those kinds of opportunities are available to every single person in the enterprise. Anyone can chart a new path, as long as it makes sense for the business and you can find a willing mentor."

Starting from the simple assumption that everyone is a manager in their own lives was a transformative one for Morning Star. Since the organization adopted its two rules, don't use force and keep commitments, it's seen amazing results, which Doug says is a testament to a favorite truism of his, by Dee Hock, founder and former CEO of Visa, that "Simple, clear purpose and principles give rise to complex and intelligent behavior. Complex rules and regulations give rise to simple and stupid behavior."

The Morning Star organizational model is a radical departure from common command-and-control systems, and more, it's wildly successful. But also, and perhaps most importantly, it illustrates that factors like "thin margins" and "seasonality," perennial excuses for why farms and farmers can't run their operations and manage their employees differently, are just that: excuses. Morning Star is a prime example that with a combination of sufficient expertise and the right motivations, organizations in food and farming can grow and be transformed into premier workplaces that respect the dignity of their employees.

A key lesson for those looking to facilitate democracy in their food or farm business: a clear vision or guiding principles is vital. Just as Ari Weinzweig from Zingerman's said, none of the organizations we've looked at don't have problems. Democracy is not a cure-all for dysfunction. What these organizations have is a shared set of priorities that are clearly defined and understood. Throughout times of hardship, conflict, and disagreement, as Ari says, problems are dealt with in "a positive, performance-oriented, values-driven, mission-focused, caring and giving way" (2010).

From that vision comes an organization's systems, which will be unique to the work you do. Developing these systems will require discussion, planning, failure, and iteration. Deep discussion of building specific systems is beyond the scope of this book, but you'll find excellent discussions of this topic throughout the recommended readings, found in the Appendix.

BECOMING US

When a food or farm business aims to create people-systems, shifting mindsets around worker dignity and democratizing the workplace are only part of the equation. Finding the right people is also critical.

Diversity, in terms of experiences, backgrounds, skill sets, and goals, is a key consideration. In addition to the benefits discussed last chapter, there are meaningful gains to diversity for farm and food system employees too. New team members not only bring new ideas and ways of thinking to the table but also different kinds of relationships to communities who have historically not been included in food or farming movements. Prioritizing diversity also creates the opportunity for more innovation and agility as well as more resiliency in the face of growing risk. More eyes and brains trained on the business, especially brains that work in different ways, are more likely to foresee and find creative and beneficial solutions to the business's problems.

Prioritizing diversity also requires serious soul searching on the part of all involved. Not only because working with a diverse team is as challenging as it is rewarding, but also because to identify the kinds of skills and experiences a team might be lacking requires honest assessment. Here we are deep in the space where only the people involved in a specific organization will know how to do this work. It will likely require discussion, bonding, growing and weathering hardship together, and may even require bringing in outside moderation to facilitate digging deeper.

The organizations we've explored in this chapter have embraced the idea that food and farm workers can be so much more than just a labor line item to be minimized. People are a business's first line of defense and its most ardent fans and believers—its heart, soul, and brain. Leaders that can motivate the right people to work in effective systems that respect their dignity will take an organization a long way. But it's also important that as circumstances change owners or employees remain ready to respond to the business's evolving needs.

Consider Patrick. With twenty-four employees on the ranch side, and nearly that in the processing plant, the business is spread all over the state of North Carolina. One result of this growth means that these days Patrick spends much more time in the office, managing the finances, selling, and working with employees. He doesn't get to spend much time with the cattle. It's hard for him to be away from the part of the operation that he loves the most, but he's accepted that reality of farm entrepreneurship.

Successful farm businesspeople like Patrick often start as technical experts (in his case, a skilled rancher), but few remain the primary source of technical expertise and labor as their businesses grow. Growth requires founders to be or find visionary leaders and excellent managers, both of which take time and mental resources that can easily crowd out technical work. Patrick prioritized the health of the business over his desire to ranch, and he's been rewarded for it, but many people who start farm businesses simply don't want to do that.

The problem with this is that, too often, leaders who prioritize doing the work they like the most fail to recruit, retain, and empower partners and teammates who can pick up the slack on other critical tasks, such as managing people, finances, or marketing. Too many leaders crave control over all aspects of the business, and however sympathetic that is from a psychological perspective, it's also a pretty effective way to throttle a business.

Michael E. Gerber's *The E-Myth Revisited* captures a key idea that shaped my understanding of the role that leaders and owners have in a farm business. Gerber writes about a hypothetical scenario in which a small business owner asks her mentor, "But what if I want to do the technical work in my business?" The mentor's response is forthright and heated:

> *Then for God's sake [...] get rid of your business! [...] You can't ignore the financial accountabilities, the marketing accountabilities, the sales and administrative accountabilities. You can't ignore your future employees' need for leadership, for purpose, for responsible management, for effective communication, for something more than just a job in which their sole purpose is to support you doing your job [...]. If all you want from a business of your own is the opportunity to do what you did before you started your business, get paid more for it, and have more freedom to come and go, your greed—I know that sounds harsh, but that's what it is—your self-indulgence will eventually consume both you and your business.*

This entreaty, here applied to a generic small business, applies to farming as well. The tendency to start a farm business to be a farmer, rather than a business owner, is a critical reason why the current model is so often unsuccessful. In short, people don't know what they're signing up for.

Lance Woodbury, the family farm advisor, has had similar conversations with farmers he's worked with. He tells a story of a conversation he once had with a farmer, during which he described the four modes that farm businesses move through—survival, stability, professionalization, and institutionalization. As he described the institutionalization process, the farmer realized that having meetings, training new employees, and ensuring that the business was ready for the future was too much "nonfarm" work. If that's what it takes to professionalize and institutionalize, the farmer decided, they would rather just sell the farm.

For farm owners who are determined to professionalize rather than quit farming altogether, becoming proficient at training, management, and mentorship is vital. In a democratized organization where employees have ownership, the role of leaders is not to be the decision-maker, the overseer, or the boss. Their role is to build consensus. This work takes a tremendous amount of practice and skill, and probably no small amount of unlearning the forceful practices of hierarchical organizations that most of us have been a part of.

Notably, this work is slow. It takes time for people to get to know one another, build trust, and develop habits and strategies around working together well. This is a good thing. Jobs that don't require familiarity, trust, or camaraderie, and organizations that treat workers like cogs that should be interchangeable, fail to respect human dignity and to take advantage of the unique skills and abilities that individuals have to offer. Expect disagreement, to have to define and redefine roles, and don't expect everyone to be cohesive on day one, ten, or even three hundred. The principles you adopt, like Morning Star's "do no harm and keep commitments," must be sturdy enough to help individuals navigate towards trust; and the role of the leader is to provide support on this long journey.

THIS IS THE HARDEST PART

Finding, training, and keeping good employees is a challenge in every business, and farming is no exception. Agriculture's particular challenges stand out because they are largely self-made. It's not that there are too few people with the skills needed to the farm; it's that participants in the ag industry have, for centuries, refused to recognize the dignity of the people who work with them, and have thus failed to pay them appropriately or provide them with other basics of fulfilling work.

This undervaluing of farm labor comes, in part, from the misconception that agriculture is an independent endeavor. The number of farmers I've met over the years whose first response to the question, "Why did you want to farm?" is, "Because I don't like people," is telling. But farming well is not, and never has been, an activity that can be done alone. It requires community. In our modern discourse about the food and farm system, "community" almost always refers to the community of customers (i.e., Community Supported Agriculture). But the community of people who work within the farm—who tend it and pour their time and talents into it every day—is just as important.

It is true, however, that in many ways the goals of a business and those of a community are not aligned. Businesses seek profit while communities seek togetherness, where members can find a role that fits. This is the needle that big team farms must try to thread, and to do so is extremely difficult. It makes sense, then, that many who attempt this work are going to fail. Therefore, know that implementing a more democratized organizational structure is something that can (and likely should) be implemented over time, leaving room for feedback, adjustments, and for the people within it to transition.

A healthy people-system is the best hope most farms have if they aim to take care of their community of customers. One farmer alone, wearing a dozen hats, can't possibly hope to grow healthy, delicious food, price it appropriately, get it to the customer at the right time, and do it all without damaging the world around them. Just as healthy plants and animals start, perhaps unexpectedly, with healthy soils, the work of feeding communities starts with taking care of food- and farmworkers.

By combining ownership and strong and diverse people systems, big team farms can create the dignified jobs that we would be proud to have and support. People with good jobs, who take pride in their work, and who feel inspired and respected are the best suited to tackle the next element of the equation: growing healthy, accessible food.

CHAPTER 3

Farms Are Food Businesses

———

It was a toasty summer afternoon when I first met Don Bustos on his farm in Española, New Mexico. The spot, Santa Cruz Farm and Greenhouses, is nestled in the southern edge of the Sangre de Cristo Mountains and has been home to Don's family for more than four hundred years.

Behind a shop and a shaded home lies three acres of produce, interspersed with scrub and wild plants in a dense thicket from which, Don points out as we pass, blackberries are spilling. As we stroll between the rows, he points out where the coyotes access the field. He advises me that they come to take their share of the harvest, as do the birds and insects. As I cast around for signs of a scarecrow or other critter-repelling tools, Don waves me off. He's not worried about losing produce to the animals. In fact, he plans on it.

"When we plant, we plant three seeds," Don shares. "One is for the neighbors, one is for God's creatures, and one is for us. So, we've got to figure out every year how we're going to give at least a third to two-thirds of our crop away."

And the thing is, he does. What's more, this very ethic has not only allowed Don to grow and maintain a successful farm for the last four decades, it has also made the farm more resilient, more community-focused, and excellent at growing food.

To achieve this, Don says, takes not only a lot of planning and research but also a profound reckoning with his personal limits. And, he notes, this isn't the only way to tackling growing and selling food. Other farms are finding different paths to their customers, but they all have something in common—they each aim to reach their communities where they already eat.

ON THE SACREDNESS OF FOOD

Food is a sacred, living thing. It is culture, comfort, love, expression, belonging, history, and legacy. Food is essential nourishment, not only for bodies but also for spirits and communities. Food is the way we break down the world around us and build ourselves up with what we've gleaned. Food is literally what we hunger for. Being able to choose, grow, cook, and eat nourishing, wholesome, and delicious food is, in my experience, one of the very best things about being alive.

This is the nature of food that we have to grapple with if we hope to build a better food system and better farm businesses. If we could start from scratch, we would first define our overall systems to respect our love of and need for food. But our current economic system generally does not acknowledge these "nonmarket" qualities of food. Instead, our system maintains two tiers of food access: one for the wealthy, and one for the rest. This system aims to reduce food to carefully targeted consumer products, on the one extreme as costly status goods often entirely divorced from place, people, and culture, and on the other as meaningless, cheap calories.

I don't know that we can make meaningful progress towards a more just food and farm system while this literally life-ending system of food apartheid is in place. We need to dismantle the systems that weaponize food access and affordability as a tool to exert force on workers, subdue and appropriate cultures considered "other," and entrench poverty. But how do we move towards this dismantlement?

I believe that, from those within and around agriculture, it requires fighting against the logic of "cheap food" as defense for lack of farm and food system oversight and the idea that poor nutrition is a consumer problem. In a world where we grow nearly one and a half times the number of calories that are needed for human survival, we should fight for the human right to food (Holt Giménez, 2014). Moving toward this dismantlement will also require that creative logistical and marketing models that get accessible food to people where they already eat be seriously considered by players throughout the food system, including consumers of all income levels.

The pressures being faced by consumers today are enormous. Food prices are rising rapidly, far outpacing increases in average income in the US (USDA ERS, 2021a). This reality offers a valuable opening for a new conversation about how we think about and provide access to nutritious food, which could be a first step towards thinking fundamentally differently about what we eat, and why.

MEETING PEOPLE WHERE THEY'RE AT

Don says his farm, and his business philosophy, started with a solid business plan, which required a ton of market research.

"We have a simple farm," he says, "and we're successful because we've identified the weaknesses in the local economies to meet fresh demand." At the start of Don's career, in the 1980s, he identified the aging back-to-the-land movement's increasing interest in organic food, which became a key first opportunity to serve local customers—"family and friends" as Don calls them. But he knew he needed more than one observation to build a business.

"When I first started doing a lot of this work, I traveled all over the United States, and I studied farmers markets and public markets. And I started to learn about how different markets survive, and how different vendors within those markets are able to adapt to the changing times and trends and needs of their local communities." This work was eye-opening for Don, and he learned one of his most important lessons while doing it—that price is everything.

"You have to know exactly how much everything is costing you. The seeds, the rents, the land, the insurances. And then you have to build all those costs into your market price and allow yourself a profit margin." Though this may sound like simple arithmetic, getting to the level of precision that allows for the kind of pricing that Don aims for required him to challenge many of the common truisms about smaller-scale farming.

He knew that other local farmers were planting twenty, thirty, or even a hundred different species and varieties. Perhaps partly because the owners enjoyed the novelty and the challenge, but also because they were willing to try almost anything a customer would ask for. Don saw this as the wrong path—growing a large and constantly shifting variety of crops meant he couldn't dial in on growing good-sellers, understanding their precise economics, or ensuring that their production wouldn't overtax his team. Instead, he's focused on a much more limited number of carefully selected crops— eight to ten per year.

"We diversify in really high-value crops that not a lot of other growers are growing in the region. So that allows us to set the market price at a reasonable rate that the consumers can afford and still allow us to be profitable. We don't compete with other growers. So, in the middle of the summer, when everybody's trying to sell cucumbers or squash, we're selling blackberries." Don's local extension agent helped him develop his plan to differentiate. Once his crops were identified, his central focus was establishing good labor and safety practices and then meeting the market demand, work that still shifts and changes year to year.

All this research and planning has not only kept Don's farm going in the high desert but also helped him put away enough resources to ensure the farm can continue to operate for years, even in the face of events like catastrophic drought. This combination of pricing, marketing, and risk management has allowed Don to pay the farm's bills for about forty years. Though there have certainly been financial difficulties, he says, the farm is still profitable, and he pays his workers a living wage.

To some readers this idea of a number-crunching, price-refining, profit-focused farmer can't possibly be the same person who's planning to give away one-third of his harvest to scavenging animals. But Don's resistance to maximization has been an incredible investment in the operation's resilience. In part because it means when he's making his plans, he knows that he'll make a profit on every carton of berries or ear of corn, rather than believing he'll "make it up in volume." It also allows him to reduce the stress and strain on himself and his team, who don't struggle with a constant need to keep fields clear of "pests" or to comb every acre looking for the last scrap of edible food to sell. This approach may sound wasteful, but building in flexibility means that nobody is working sixty- or seventy-hour weeks, even during the height of the season; there's no broken bodies and no toughing it out for the sake of profit.

I ask Don whether this strategy limits his ability to make his produce accessible to those beyond the high-end foodie scene. He says he hasn't had a problem finding that sweet spot, in part because he's competing in a market niche, one he saw that no one else did.

"We try to provide the appropriate food for the community. So, in Santa Fe, people love the gourmet greens, like arugula, these beautiful microgreens, exotic greens, eggplants, peppers. They're really beautiful visually and very tastefully appealing. And that's where you get your high-end price points. And then in the valley [in Española, where Don lives], people love to eat squash, cucumbers, green chili, and sweet corn." Differentiating the markets and identifying differing wants and needs helped Don to carve out his niche, which is defined by getting people the produce they prize at an unusual time and price point they appreciate.

In a world where "pay-what-you-can"-type food models are attractive to many as a way to increase food access, Don can implement that very model without sacrificing income the farm needs to survive. For example, he charges as much as $12/pound for prized microgreens in the wealthier Santa Fe, but when he's in the lower-income valley, he sells squash for $.89/pound. His margin varies from product to product, and lower margins in some markets can be accommodated with higher margins in others. But this means the premium

Don earns results from his ability to match fruits and vegetables to his customer's expectations.

"You really have to identify and understand your customers and try to sell them what they love to eat. My neighbors like to eat squash and really know how to prepare it well. So, we're not trying to sell them $12 lettuce; we're selling them the squash they want at a price that both they and we can afford. But that's always the hardest to do [...]. It's a balancing act." Don knows that there is no income threshold on loving food. He's found plenty of community members across the income spectrum willing to pay more for the right product at the right time than they would at the grocery.

"People don't mind paying for good food. Food is the most important thing there is, so they'll pay what it's worth if you're not trying to gouge them."

Don's experience farming in one of the country's poorest, driest, and most rural states, offers insight on what can be achieved in terms of feeding people. He shows that what it takes is creativity, a willingness to do what other people don't, a lot of thoughtfulness and listening, and an unapologetic focus on gaining enough profit to meet his need without running himself or his team ragged.

For many interested in food system work, profit is a dirty word. But businesses, farms included, simply cannot exist in the long-term without making some. In our current system, the demand that selling food be a low-profit to no-profit enterprise only makes life worse for workers, on farms, in processing plants, and in the wholesale and retail sectors. But Don's experience shows that it's possible to make enough money to thrive, treat workers with dignity, and subscribe to a meaningful ethic to respect land and life. What it requires is limits—and as we'll discuss in the next chapter—setting those limits is something big team farmers and farm businesses must prioritize.

THE MARKET WE MAKE

Don still transacts most of his sales at various farmers markets around the region, making him an exception among the farmers I've met. He's also personally done a lot of work to grow and develop his regional farmers markets. Don's four decades at the farmers market are unusual mainly because most farmers I've met have lost their excitement for farmers markets much, much sooner.

Most aspiring or early stage farmers get the impression that farmers markets *must* be a great place to meet customers, make sales, build a brand, and learn through interaction and observation in the marketplace. Why else would they be so popular? Yet of all the ways experience in farming shifts perspectives, few are starker, from what I've seen, then the way veteran farmers change their opinion on farmers markets.

Overwhelmingly, farmers who are just starting out love the market. They love the vibes and the community they feel it creates. They savor the opportunity to get off the farm once or twice a week, to meet their customers face-to-face, to build relationships and understanding, and to check in with friends and neighbors.

A few years in, this optimism is usually long gone. I've found that most experienced farmers have had enough 4:00 a.m. harvests and long drives just to spend another morning in blistering or frigid weather, explaining to yet another customer decked out in designer goods why their tomatoes are twice as expensive as the ones at the local chain grocery store, only to bring most of the produce back, and making just a few hundred dollars for their trouble.

It turns out those vibes are for wealthy shoppers, not for frustrated and exhausted vendors. The community of markets is too often a sort of tyranny, with petty organizers delivering threats and slapping on fines for five minutes' tardiness, needing to leave a little early, or for any other infractions of the obscure and arbitrary rules. There are undoubtedly good customers to meet at farmers markets but most farmers I've met find that, unless they carved out a unique, timely, profitable niche for themselves early, the luster of being a farmer at a farmers' market very quickly wears off.

Robert, a Southwestern citrus grower, offered his analysis on farmers markets bluntly. "Ecologically speaking, it's total bullshit. Farmers markets are not a solution; they're a bougie tourist trap." He argues that whether you're evaluating environmental, economic, or even community access metrics, farmers markets are simply not an effective way to distribute food.

"Each producer has to deliver their food to the market, and then every shopper drives to that market. And in order to cross off their entire shopping list, chances are they have to attend two or three of those markets to get everything." Robert believes that between these transport inefficiencies, the waste of unsold food, and the fact that people often can't attend markets when they're held or can't afford the food sold there, farmers markets are often a lousy counter to current alternatives like the grocery store. Though he's not a fan of big box stores either, Robert grudgingly admires that they have mastered logistics, and believes that farmers who want to grow successful businesses will have to gain that expertise too.

Farmers markets have been painted as a way for farmers and consumers to team up and take on the major players in the food system. Though there has been significant growth in the ubiquity of farmers markets in recent decades, they're often a crapshoot for both sellers and buyers (Jacobs, 2017). It's true that there are great farmers out at the market who are making great food, and patronizing their operations could be a positive way to support your community. But the prices many farmers need to charge are so high compared to alternatives that even the most conscious consumers can't justify paying them. Farmers markets are too often a kind of performance space where shoppers pay a premium for the market experience, while producers either represent hobby farms or are struggling to make the economics of attending markets work. Farmers markets suffer from resiliency issues as well—with everything from inclement weather to road construction having significant impacts on attendance.

Consider the scope alone—US retail grocery is a nearly $700 billion sector annually (USDA ERS, 2021b). Farmers markets in the US might transact around $2.5 billion annually (NSAC, 2020). In short, retail grocery, among other avenues, are systems that big team food and farm businesses must participate in if their goal is to feed people. Despite years of growth, farmers markets have yet to have a meaningful impact on that system and likely aren't going to cut it.

If the goal is to actually feed people, it's crucial to meet the community where it is—geographically, culturally, and financially. It's also way harder than applying for a market and showing up there one day a week. But to serve our communities the kind of healthy, accessible food they need, we have to look beyond the conventional "small farm" sales and marketing channels to where people shop: in grocery stores and, increasingly, online.

One strategy is to cut out the market altogether and go to customers directly.

GROW A NEW MARKET

Patrick Robinette, from Harris-Robinette Beef in North Carolina, took a longer road to understand his market than Don did.

"My original inclination was that I had no desire to feed the hippies," he explained, describing his early career. "We don't do grass-fed beef; we feed corn to animals." His mindset started to shift when a mentor pointed out the high efficiencies being achieved by other ranchers with the grass-fed model in the West, and Patrick sensed an opportunity in the lush greenery of his Southeastern home. Twenty years ago he wrote a plan that has slowly evolved into a complex business. Today, the operation is entirely grass-fed and finished, and he hasn't used synthetic fertilizers or other chemicals in decades.

As Patrick started to see his production plans come together, he felt that the real opportunity lay in direct-to-market beef, selling from the farm directly to consumers rather than to a wholesaler. He had to figure out his own processing and logistics first, but he found that the profit margins were worth the effort.

By 2012, the farm was selling about forty head of cattle a week and outsourcing to three different processing facilities to get it done. The demand was there, and Patrick took the leap and set up Micro Summit Processors. That piece of the puzzle, he says, clinched the farm's sustainability by adding resiliency.

"For processors or retailers, their losses are short-term. If something goes wrong, they might take a hit, but they can also just buy more cattle. My losses go all the way back to three years ago when we bred that cow, and we did the gestation for nine months, we got the calf on the ground, and then we raised it up, and thirty-three months goes by before I get paid. If something goes wrong in that final stage, at the processor, I lose it all." This issue hit Patrick particularly hard in 2012 when one of the processors he was working with mixed up an order and cut eighteen cattle that were destined for butcher shops into individual retail cuts, leaving his customers high and dry and saddling him with thousands of pounds of unsold meat.

Patrick's business also illustrates that it's not simply about starting up a new business or finding a gimmick, it's about having a vision with an exacting eye towards ensuring profitability. This approach allowed him to expand on his original plan. Most recently that entailed cutting out the middlemen he worked with to deliver his meat, a change that involved setting up an entire logistics operation within the farm business.

"We've created a system where we can get fresh meat anywhere in the world in about forty-eight hours," he explains, "at a very reasonable cost. And it costs us less than the markup we'd otherwise pay to distributors and brokers." This undertaking was a heavy lift, but it's already returning value. Though he's built the capacity to access both national and international markets, in the long-term he's focused on serving his meat closer to home.

"If we go to a regional food system, the removal of the mileage of the trucks on the highway, I believe, will significantly lessen the greenhouse gasses," he argues. This idea fits into a larger evolution in thought about his customers—the same person who started out disdainful of marketing to "hippies" is now working with advocates around the Green New Deal, seeking alliances with the Humane Society on animal welfare, and preaching about the many benefits of raising meat on grass. To wit, Micro Summit has even moved away from petroleum-based plastic packaging and instead adopted plant-based alternatives. Patrick sees this as an essential move to get ahead because eventually, either due to regulation, consumer demand, or other market necessity, these kinds of upgrades will become the norm.

"We've got to quit talking about how crazy people are," Patrick told me when I asked about his perspective on advocates aiming to create a more just food system. "Accept them for who they are and then work our systems to what their beliefs are [...]. Raise the product that people want."

So many of Patrick's efforts come back to this critical insight: putting his customers' needs and wants before his own. Yet there's another key element that both Patrick and Don share that, paradoxically, helps curtail the impulse to chase after every customer's whim. The counterbalance to the edict to grow what people want is to also grow what you can grow well. Even better, grow something, anything, that only you can grow.

GROW SOMETHING NEW

I get the impression talking to Bob Quinn that he didn't mean to become the de facto face of an ancient grain.

"When we started, we thought it would be a novelty," he told me by phone from his home in Montana. "People said it came out of King Tut's tomb and I thought, Oh, man, this'll be fun." But since the start of his experiment in the late 1980s, he's grown a successful company and a global market around

KAMUT, his brand name for Khorasan wheat, an ancient Mesopotamian grain.

Over the course of three decades, the farm went from growing a half-acre of Khorasan wheat to one hundred thousand acres, contracted through two hundred and fifty organic farms in Montana and adjacent Canadian provinces, and has earned a loyal following throughout the US and Europe as an exceptionally flavorful pasta flour.

Not only was Bob interested in growing an unusual grain, he also wanted to grow an unusual business to match. He decided to avoid working with the long stream of middlemen and gatekeepers who turn raw farm products into food, and instead opted to maintain ownership over nearly every step of KAMUT's journey from the field to the kitchen. This led him to start his company, Montana Flour & Grain, which originally sold wheat of all kinds directly off the farm. That effort took Bob to food shows and to continuous customer interactions, where he learned from shoppers and fans about the interest in organic food. He then made the transition on his farm to organic production. The business grew slowly for many years, but it wasn't until a KAMUT-based pasta enthralled a gluten-sensitive friend that he realized how big an opportunity he'd found.

"We thought, 'Oh my gosh, this is something very special. It's like a gift from the creator or something.' We realized this is more than just marketing. This is something that can help people." The first step for Bob was to set up a processing business, given that the commodity grain channels (i.e., the local elevator) wouldn't buy this unconventional grain. He got a local friend to quit their job and become his miller. Bob says, though he enjoys the thrill of trying something new, he's always been careful to trial projects at a scale small enough not to put the whole farm in jeopardy. He aims for pilots big enough to build on, pending success, but small enough to abandon and move on if it doesn't pan out.

"We started out responding to requests for organic and stone-ground flour. I suggested putting stone mills in bakeries, so they'd have it fresh, but they didn't want to do that. So we did, and it gave us a platform on which to build our business." Bob says that maintaining profitability along the way was always a balancing act. The premium on high-protein, organic wheat was the foundation for everything, and then selling flour instead of just the raw wheat added another dimension of value and margin. Bob says the flour mill itself, which was an independent LLC, was meant to be a break-even enterprise long-term, but he was able to leverage it into a significant amount of profitability for the farm.

"We can build whole communities, not just a single farm," he says. "It's about a community being successful. And that's what we've tried to do over the years." He isn't just paying lip service to this idea either: the farm and its related businesses currently support twelve families, increasing the population of its hometown of Big Sandy, Montana, by 5 to 6 percent.

Marketing KAMUT has come naturally to Bob because he's been able to respond to significant demand for novelty and quality in the market. The product sold itself, particularly in the Italian pasta market. Even when Bob refused to offer major buyers a volume discount ("We charge everyone a fair price at which we're profitable, not just big buyers," he says), it didn't dissuade them from giving it a try.

"They just went for it," he says, "We're just trying to keep up with demand."

Today, Bob has largely retired from his direct work on the farm. He leases his farmland to two of his former employees, who carry on the work he started. Since retiring, Bob has put together a world conference on landrace ancient wheats, written a book, and continued developing a snack food and oil business with the KAMUT brand. He's looking to sell the brand to his employees. Now he's working on building an organic research center on six hundred acres of his farm, where he's exploring not only grain production but also dryland fruit and vegetable production in the Montana biome.

The best advice Bob has for farmers looking to build a business—it's all in your mind-set. "I've told anyone who would listen that I don't raise a single commodity on my farm. The only thing I raised is good food for people's health, enjoyment, and the betterment of the community and the planet as a whole." He's found that farmers, himself included, always work hard to prove themselves right, whether they believe something will or won't work.

Bob's story highlights the opportunity for a farm to create a new market for its unique product. Though this idea is common further up the food chain (see the near-infinite flow of novelty snacks and beverages), it is uncommon in the farm business context. In the commodity production space, there is an overwhelming sense that there are only a few, generic crops to choose from, and that even among those only some really make financial or ecological sense. But the "small farm" space is not immune either. A perceived lack of "practical" options is why every vendor at the farmers market has a mountain of carrots and radishes in the early summer and it feels like every CSA is just nine pounds of cherry tomatoes in August. It's why every vendor sells eggs and why—despite the distaste that many small and beginning farmers have for industrial ag—I know very few farmers who aren't selling Cornish Cross broilers, the pinnacle of industrially optimized chicken genetics.

Yet we can look around food and farming spaces and see that finding profitable niches is possible. KAMUT's story shows that even at the scale of commodity grains, there's space to explore, experiment, and carve out new and transformative markets. Grass-fed beef might not be as much of a differentiator today as it was twenty years ago, but now Patrick can have it on your doorstep by the day after tomorrow. And he can guarantee its quality, safety, and profitability from cow to fridge. Don might be growing relatively common varieties of produce but, by paying attention to the nuances of his customer's needs, fine-tuning his production to have product available when other growers don't, and meticulously refining his price points, he's made his off-season blackberries just as unique a product as KAMUT snack foods or next-day Carolina meats.

These farm businesses are each pursuing different objectives on their path to growing profitable food and farm businesses. Though the commonalities among them are critical—the profound care for their customers, their own competencies, a rigorous approach to profitability, and an interest in and excitement for marketing and sales—the differences between these stories are important too. These differences demonstrate that there isn't one way to grow a food or farm business that can deliver healthy and accessible food to people. Every farm organization will find its own unique niche.

Of course, not every idea will work either. I've heard countless stories of farms investing in various value-added ideas that end up failing. Novelty isn't its own panacea;

pursuing a new idea, market, or customer base is not a silver bullet for success. Other pieces must be in place—engaged and passionate people-systems chief among them—before any food business idea, no matter how good, can come to fruition.

One of those increasingly important aspects has to do with how crops or other food products are grown. It's easy to make a marketing claim about production and believe that it will help sell your product, but it often proves much more complicated to bring that claim to life on the farm. That's why, on big team farms, good environmental outcomes have to be more than sloganeering or marketing spin. Good environmental outcomes must be part of the organization's DNA.

CHAPTER 4

The Limit Does Exist

In between the megamansions that lounge along the hillsides outside Los Angeles, I spent a scorching August day tromping through bone-dry brush with a couple of shepherds.

Jack and Jenya, the shepherds in question, live a little over an hour north of the city along the California coast. They own Cuyama Lamb, a grazing business that, at peak season, is home to several hundred ewes and lambs which are shorn for wool and harvested for meat.

A generic California sheep flock is not what brought me out to this dusty arroyo, flanked on all sides by million-dollar vacation homes and exclusive wellness retreat spaces. Jack and Jenya were poking around in this particular forty acres of steep scrubland because they were hired to graze their sheep there by the local fire department, as a form of wildfire prevention.

"Fire mitigation work in California is just expanding so much right now," Jack told me when we first spoke over the phone. "So we're coming into this field at a moment where people have done the groundwork. [It's acknowledged that] small ruminant grazing can be an incredibly effective means of targeting [fuel loads] in areas where communities are endangered." A surprising amount of Jack and Jenya's time in their last five years of farming has been spent participating in these conversations, and working not with meat customers or landowners but with municipal governments and others looking to restore balance to landscapes through biological rather than chemical or mechanical means.

Grazing to combat invasive species or for fire-suppression turns the script of land access on its head. Rather than paying a landlord to graze animals on rented ground, Cuyama Lamb gets paid to occupy space. But naturally, the story is more complicated than that.

We were out surveying ahead of the sheep because this chunk of "backcountry" is steep and overgrown. It'll be up to Jack and Jenya to build some temporary fencing, develop a grazing plan to guide the herd's movement through the whole area, and ensure the adventurous lambs don't end up vulnerable to predators, on roadways, or hanging out around Oprah's pool.

And the logistical challenges of making the space ready for a flock are just the beginning. Though Jack and Jenya's sheep are hardy and good at navigating perilous terrain, their sheep still need enough calories every day to stay healthy, plus access to clean water.

"Trying to be a contract grazing service and grow good meat is not an easy thing to combine," Jack reports, given that many of the areas they're paid to graze are little more than tinderboxes of parched plants that don't offer much in the way of ovine nutrition. Not to mention that moving around on steep and rocky terrain takes more out of the sheep than loafing around in a flat pasture. Despite the challenges, Jack and Jenya are working toward a vision of a regional meat and wool production system that isn't dependent on the dehumanized economies of scale represented by feedlots and mega-slaughter plants, but instead depends on many people tending landscapes intimately.

"To do this work," Jack tells me, "You need people who are on the ground, who are making a lot of really responsive decisions, who are in relationship and communication with a lot of folks." And in between dusty treks, this is precisely what we're doing; driving around the neighborhood, knocking on doors, talking to soon-to-be neighbors about sheep and fire prevention, building familiarity and trust, sharing phone numbers, and comparing notes on the landscape. This is complex community work, and it's every bit a competency of this farming operation as putting up fences and moving the sheep.

Jack and Jenya certainly did not invent the idea of grazing as a service, and they freely admit that they still have a lot to learn. But the model they've landed on, and the way they're pursuing it, I think, highlights a mind-set shift that's critical for any farm business looking to put good environmental outcomes at the center of their organization.

That shift is a recognition that "good environmental outcomes" aren't achieved by following the organic standards or planting a "regenerative" market garden. It starts long before a crop is selected and must be a much more significant part of an organization than sticking a simple label or claim on the final product. Stewardship and land-tending can't be reserved for "when the farm gets big enough" either. Like profit, stewardship must be built into every unit and activity, and it must represent an end in itself, not something that will somehow magically unlock when a farm reaches a certain scale.

As relatively new farmers, Jack and Jenya didn't have the cash to purchase land (let alone housing) in one of the wealthiest communities in America. But they refused to use "we don't own this land" as an excuse not to protect and care for it. Sheep and other ruminant ungulates have long been a part of the local ecology. So Jack and Jenya knew that the species could be part of restoring balance on their drying landscape with thoughtful and appropriate management. The pair and their team have had to be creative to keep the sheep in good health on degraded land and have developed systems that lead to acceptable outcomes in terms of animal health. Part of this process required balancing trade-offs; recognizing that every lamb was not going to be top-grade or reach its maximum possible weight, and that was okay because selling meat is just one income stream of several that contributes to the farm's bottom line.

For those interested in a deep reflection on the universal value of the latest regenerative agriculture craze, perhaps Jack and Jenya's story feels disappointing. No black soil, no verdant expanses, no harmonious animals rotating with lush plants in a veritable garden of Eden. Just some shepherds in a big ditch trying to figure out how to feed sheep and reduce the wildfire fuel load at the same time. But given that there are many more ditches, deserts, swamps, hillsides, mountain tops, plains, and scrub- and woodlands than there are garden-like expanses in the world, I think we must start our conversation about growing in collaboration, rather than in competition, with natural systems with the understanding that the end goal of "good environmental outcomes" is unlikely to look similar from one geography to the next.

In fact, a healthy and generous food landscape on the California coast might not contain a single speck of black soil or emerald greenery. Just as a fruitful wetland full of plant and animal nutrients might look like a rotten and decaying ecosystem when compared to a temperate grassland. By the same standards, a mountain or hillside covered in berries and supporting fisheries and grazing might be described as "unfarmable" due only to its grade and elevation, but in no way does this mean it is not a healthy and productive ecosystem capable of feeding people.

The first step in understanding how big team farms might contribute to good environmental outcomes, then, is to vastly expand what we perceive farming to be. From my perspective, farming is simply the managed production and harvesting of plants and animals for food, fiber, and fuel. Farming well is to do this work without fundamentally disrupting the ecosystem within which the farm exists.

ON THE SACREDNESS OF OUR WORLD

The world we live in is a sacred, living place. The plants, animals, forces, and objects that inhabit it shape our reality and, in turn, who we are. Earth is our home, and those who cohabitate with us are our extended family, genetically and spiritually. In all the universe, only we are Earthlings, willingly and unwillingly sharing in the resources that have made us all. Being a part of the grander interconnectedness of life is a solace and one of the few true wellsprings of meaning. Having the chance to live, breathe, feel the sun, look to the horizon, bear witness to plant and animal life, and to feel certain that we are and will forever be part of something infinite, that's everything.

This is the nature of world that we have to grapple with if we hope to build a better food system. If we were able to start from scratch, we would first define our overall economic systems to respect this world, and our place within it. But instead, our current system motivates maximum extraction from our world, exhausting places and people for profit at an ever-increasing rate. This system aims to reduce our world to the sum of its salable resources, breaking down complex systems into finite parts, destroying synergies for the sake of private gain, and abandoning the broken remains to future generations.

I don't know that we can make meaningful progress towards a more just food and farm system while this Earth-threatening extraction continues. We need to dismantle the systems that alter, manipulate, and destroy everything, from the very genetic blueprints of life to entire watersheds and rain forests, with a consciousness of nothing but private wealth accumulation. But how do we move towards this dismantlement?

I believe it requires those within and around agriculture to reject the free pass to avoid public oversight embodied in the idea that "farmers are the original environmentalists," along with the idea that farming *more* is going to be a solution to climate change. We must simultaneously fight in favor of more, and more strictly enforced, environmental rules for agriculture. Reaching dismantlement will also require deep questioning of the current theory of farm production, and broader discussion and acceptance of the idea that feeding people is about much more than just farming.

The pressures being faced by the climate and ecosystems around the globe today are intense. Agricultural production in general remains one of the top contributors to the climate crisis, not only as a result of emissions but also through the threat it poses to biodiversity and vulnerable habitats. The risks agriculture poses to the climate, and vice versa, offer a valuable opportunity to have a different conversation about how we procure food from our landscapes—which could be a first step towards a transformation in our collective understanding of our place in the world.

IT'S NOT (JUST) WHAT YOU THINK

In many ways, sound environmental stewardship can seem diametrically opposed to farming.

Superficially, it makes sense. Humans need to eat, so we extract nutrients from a nutrient-cycling system, and in doing so it seems almost necessary that the system degrades over time. But this conclusion only makes sense if we think of humans as exogenous to the system. It suggests that we stand apart from the natural world and can reach into the isolated bubble of cycling calories and energy, pull out what we want, and destroy or otherwise dispose of the waste, like a kid putting a quarter into a gumball machine.

Historically, the invention of agriculture was likely the first step in the creation of this extractive worldview. For centuries, the dichotomy between "Man and Nature" has been a European cultural, philosophical, and religious standby. But encounters with other cultures who hold no such assumptions, combined with everything modern science has taught us about our place in the universe, reveals that there is no such separation. Humans are nature.

In light of this false separation, before we plan to farm we have to first interrogate what we think we know. Some permaculture and regenerative agriculture techniques, for example, reflect our desire to be active and intentional system managers. And yet the ambition to nurture and build soils, to grow healthy and nutritious plants and animals that don't injure water, air, or adjacent ecosystems, has in some cases led to problematic outcomes. How can that be? Perhaps it's because these new farming methods, when practiced from the place of separation as benevolent over-lords of plants, animals, and resources, fall flat and lead to unintended consequences.

It's not enough, then, to change our practices—hearts and minds have to change too. Randy Woodley, who's currently farming in Yamhill, Oregon, offered some perspective on this deeper issue.

"One of the things I notice is the force, the Creator, evo-lution, whatever, it builds in open systems that are adaptable. Closed systems are what we call 'order', when humans build stuff differently than nature builds them. [But in systems beyond our control] there's this unity and diversity within everything, from the multiverse to the smallest subatomic particles. There's no singular." This perspective, Randy says, is the one that humans in general, and farmers in particular, should take when thinking about building systems. "As soon as we build these models and say this is a closed system, it will either fall apart eventually or some adaptable system will take over. That's how nature works." From Randy's per-spective, the best a farmer can do is mimic open, natural systems and integrate themselves into existing ones when-ever possible.

This resonates with the work that Jack and Jenya are doing. They could have bought ground, tilled it up, amended the soil, extracted groundwater, and planted a market garden with farmers market favorites. These farms exist in their area. They might have even been able to do this growing "organically" or even following "regenerative" practices. Instead, they started by looking at the ecosystem they were already a part of and determined what kind of plants and animals the landscape was already supporting.

Light, four-legged ungulates like sheep are long-standing inhabitants of their coastal chaparral. Sheep seem a good candidate when considering the climatic and ecological limitations, as they can move when hyper-local conditions change, as they often do in the microclimates along the coast. They're lighter on the thin soils than cattle and aren't as prone to loitering around the watering hole. They're sure-footed on steep arroyos, they're fierce mothers when protecting young from local predators, and they're willing to eat an incredible spread of plants and helpfully tramp down even more.

The sheep, in other words, don't require an artificially closed system for their survival. Instead, they can be integrated into the landscape and deliberately guided toward areas where their grazing of invasive- or over-populated species, hoof-based soil aeration, and dung-fertilization can nourish, rather than degrade, the local community. Notably, when the herd is removed from this arroyo after several weeks, the ecosystem will not take seasons and seasons to recover from extractive and exhaustive farming, but instead may be closer to a restored balance than it was prior to their arrival.

For big team farms striving for good environmental outcomes, the work must be this deep and complex. There's no simple list of practices to implement or chemicals and equipment that can't be used. The ideal end goal should not be an idealized "garden of Eden" standard but for farmland to be as indistinguishable from nearby non-farmland as possible.

Ricardo Salvador of the Union of Concerned Scientists fleshed this idea out for me in a powerful way, describing how a big team might consider the ultimate goals of their farming practices.

"The models that we have of some of the most productive ecosystems on the planet," he told me as we chatted in his DC office, "they all share very similar characteristics. First of all, they're biodiverse. The significance of biodiversity is not just that it's some virtuous ecological descriptor. Biodiversity means that all of the spaces, what ecologists call niches, are filled." The push and pull between the many species in these niches keeps nutrients and other precious resources flowing through the system, and through continuous fluctuations and adjustments the whole can achieve long-term balance.

The contrast to this complexity and diversity is a mono-crop system—a field of corn or pecan trees, or a barn full of chickens—which Ricardo says seems highly productive by the animals- or bushels-per-acre metric but is, in reality, a biological desert with only one species. All other species, so-called weeds and pests, have to be exterminated. This process leaves ecological niches vacant, requiring farmers to pay for substitutes: they apply chemical fertilizers, import bees to pollinate, or keep weeds, bugs, and disease in check with chemicals or genetic modification. The total nutrients and resources that cycle through a mono-crop system pale in comparison to biodiverse counterparts.

"In a biodiverse system, you would have organisms populating the soil and doing jobs like breaking down organic residue and turning it into organic matter. That then increases the fertility of the soil and its capacity to retain water in a way that can prevent crops from drowning and that can temporarily store water that can then be released as crops need it."

Ricardo describes a nature-mimicking field ag system would build upward from there:

"You would have your main crop, but there are so many niches that are empty in a typical mono-crop. So, you could also add some very thick-leaved crop that grows horizontally on the soil's surface, which protects it and requires very little light. You could have a crop that grows around the periphery of the crop space and occupies the niche that absorbs light and provides shade. You could have a crop that grows on the scaffolding that an annual crop like corn produces, filling another niche. And all that biodiversity then provides additional niches for organisms like insects. The majority of insects actually tend to be beneficial or, when you have a complete ecosystem, they prey on one another in such a way that they create population balance while they provide ecological services, like pollination."

The idea that insects and other "pests" should be a part of a regenerative cropping system often leads to objections from farmers, saying they can't financially stomach the losses they incur from bugs and weeds. But I'm reminded that Don Bustos has managed to achieve profitability and stability on his farm despite sharing his berries with the coyotes, birds, and bugs and of Bob Quinn's wisdom that, "Farmers work hard to prove themselves right."

Though Ricardo is optimistic that these kinds of bio-diverse systems could take shape on farms, he's worried that the current discourse around regenerative agriculture is not focused on this kind of work. It's distracted instead by an obsession with individual practices like cover cropping or crop rotations and using these practices at scale. He acknowledges that these practices can be part of open and diverse systems, but they are not enough. Cover crops in particular can easily be monocultures in sequence rather than true diversification, leading to negligible change. And negligible change at scale, obviously, remains negligible. It's crucial, Ricardo says, to combine insects, animals, plants, and both annuals and perennials, in space and time, and aiming for these complex systems usually requires less focus on individual practices and more on shifting mind-sets.

"The more perennial the balance and mix of species," Ricardo says, "the more resilient the system is, and the more carbon is being captured. And this is how we want agriculture to be performing. What I see as an end stage is a biodiverse, self-regulated polyculture system that features perennials as some of the main components." Essentially, what he envisions is what we might think of as a "wild" system, one that might persist even in the absence of human intervention. Notably, his vision is not of cover crops on every field, as one practice does not a biodiverse system make.

Naturally, there are many barriers to this work—ideological, cultural, and economic opposition chief among them. But Randy Woodley sees this struggle as a sacred one. For him, it is impossible to divorce spirituality from the actions of caring for plants, animals, and people. "It's not that we're taking something that's not spiritual and joining it with something spiritual and saying, 'Oh, we're integrating them.' It's that everything is spiritual, everything is sacred, all living things. And that means everything, even rocks, are sacred in some way and have a purpose in our world. We're part of the great community of creation, from the rock to the eagle to the person to the hippopotamus, and we all serve our purpose."

"Human beings," he continues, "we go around with a question mark on our forehead that says, 'What is our purpose?' We're taught, as Cherokee people [...] that our purpose is to maintain harmony on the earth. Our purpose is to maintain balance so that everything else can stay in harmony." Randy admits that most humans are not doing a very good job right now. "Our Harmony Way, in Cherokee, is called Eloheh," Randy says, meaning the way of balance or beauty (Eloheh is also the name of Randy's farm). "When we try to live in that, it's not this utopian destination; it is a way of living that's not perfect. But it's trying to bring our world, ourselves, and others into balance. And that's a very spiritual task." The way we farm, Randy says, is not separate from this task, but is a part of it.

Though good things are happening in the regenerative movement, Randy says, too many of the distinctions made in Western-led agriculture still sound wrong to Indigenous ears. They miss the point that is obvious to and ingrained in Indigenous worldviews, which engage in the spirituality of all living things as opposed to the dualism that keeps humans separate from nonhuman. For example, though modern practices may be steps in the right direction, they still distinguish unhelpfully between weeds and crops and often treat animals as mere objects rather than beings. Randy says the way to reconcile these shortcomings is to more directly acknowledge the sacredness of all things.

"Animals [for example] are spiritual. Before we would kill an animal, it'd have a good life, right up until its last eight seconds. And then we have a ceremony, and I raised my kids participating in that so that they can understand that it costs something when you take a life, and you have to be thankful for it. You can't just wantonly go grab a hamburger and say, 'Oh, it's just a hamburger.' No, it costs an animal its life [...]. So it's also the growing, the planting, the praying over, the celebrating. It's all part of our life cycle that's sacred and spiritual." Randy offers a fundamentally different way to think about farming and food production, not as a scheme to outsmart natural systems, but leading with spirits and hearts and approaching our role in the system with humility.

DECONSTRUCTING REGENERATION

One of the hardest parts of embracing landscape stewardship is recognizing that good outcomes come from caretaking and collaborating with natural systems rather than managing or controlling them. It's possible to create a clear, step-by-step guide or checklist to establish control. But caretaking and collaboration require an entirely customized approach, which starts by understanding where you are and who you're with. There's no one set of practices, rule of thumb, or other heuristic that applies to all food production in all places. Every farm and farmer, every plant and animal, and every practice and decision should be finely tuned to the specific geography, climate, participants, and resources available. This work is hard and requires a lot of skill, and as the effects of climate change become more unpredictable, more and more hardworking, highly skilled people will be required to do it well.

Though we've learned that much of our current agricultural system will be unsustainable in the future, this doesn't mean that land should never be cultivated or planted to just a few crops, that technology is always harmful, or that livestock must not be domesticated. Like so many others, both the dichotomy between farming and not farming and between ultramodern farming and ancient methods are false. There are no true binaries. There are infinite possibilities.

Our responsibility is not to take everything we've inherited and use it as tradition dictates without question, nor is it to abandon everything we've learned in recent years. Our responsibility is to sort through it all honestly and with humility, keep what is beneficial, what makes us more human, and abandon those ideas that keep us at arm's length from our landscapes and each other.

If you wanted to come out of this book with a handy bumper sticker slogan, this conclusion is probably infuriating. There's no easy fix. There's no trendy word or catchy idea that captures the entirety of this work. As Randy acknowledged, procuring food from the landscape is an activity that defies categorization. It's farming, but not just farming. And learning how to live in that soup of vagueness is part of the work too, and part of the fun.

The good news is that farmers all over the country and around the world are doing the work already. Some are preserving or developing silvo-agriculture systems: growing fruit- and nut-bearing trees combined with grazing or browsing livestock, and perhaps even with vegetable or medicinal plants growing in sun traps and shade. Others are helping reestablish grassland ecosystems by mixing and rotating perennial grasses with grains that, through seed saving and perpetuation on the land, are becoming landraces, a kind of native species. Still others are working in wetlands and deserts, exploring that work of ancient farmers who, in some cases, perfected tending food-producing ecosystems in spaces that colonial and imperial agriculture considered marginal or worthless. Some common threads amongst these more environmentally sound forms of food production: they rely on diverse plants and animals and do not avoid or destroy but instead integrate themselves into natural systems. They are also sensitive to a time horizon measured in decades and centuries rather than single seasons.

These farmers are not universally eschewing pesticides or genetic engineering; they don't discount modern livestock breeds because they are not heritage or "authentic." They don't insist that equipment and technology have no place in their operations, and they don't dismiss the knowledge created by modern science out of hand. When these farmers encounter a possible tool, they explore it, experiment with it, and decide whether it has a place, a beneficial niche. If it doesn't, they leave it behind.

Author Robin Wall Kimmerer, in her seminal work *Braiding Sweetgrass*, tells a brief story about a plant her people call white man's footstep, *Plantago major*, or the common plantain. "It arrived with the first settlers and followed them everywhere they went," she writes. "At first, the Native people were distrustful of a plant that came with so much trouble trailing behind." But her Indigenous ancestors didn't begrudge the plant its roots, so to speak, and instead set out to learn and understand it. They found that it had much to contribute, as sustenance and versatile medicine. It was useful, fitting into the preexisting system and adding more than it detracted.

"The wise and generous plant, faithfully following the people, became an honored member of the plant community. It's a foreigner, an immigrant, but after five hundred years of living as a good neighbor, people forget that kind of thing." She describes other immigrants, in whose footsteps we should not follow: invasive species that poison soil, hog water, and grow without regard to the limits of the ecosystem. The plantain, she writes, "is not indigenous but 'naturalized.'"

"Being naturalized to place means to live as if this is the land that feeds you, as if these are the streams from which you drink that build your body and fill your spirit." This is what it must mean to farm in a way that's good for the environment, not to be "sustainable" or "regenerative," to check a box or win the approval of a third-party auditor, but to be naturalized. To have our actions and decisions be driven not by profit or prestige but by the knowledge that stewardship of our environment, our home, is an end in itself. And not just in an ideal world either—in this world, where the difference between having a safe home or not is the difference between life and death. For previous generations, the threat of climate change might have been one "for future generations." That is no longer the case—we are their future generation; it is our lives and world that hangs in the balance.

We've proven ourselves largely unworthy of fulfilling the lofty promises that the term "regenerative" inspires, especially when we insist on carrying it out on an individual or farm level. The term generally belies an assumption that we are above, beyond, or outside natural systems in a way that allows us to tinker with their inner workings without feeling the impacts ourselves. This assumption is out of touch with the reality of being a good land steward. Our place on the landscape is not as an all-knowing creator and controller but as one moving piece in a grand system that's quite literally beyond our ability to comprehend fully.

Though our altruistic desires to regenerate and improve, to shape nature in novel ways that we think are beneficial, may be well-intentioned, the long-term outcomes of such efforts are complex and difficult to predict. A good rule of thumb is to always be skeptical of the suggestion that we've got anything "all figured out" in farming, because participating in natural systems is a truly unpredictable endeavor. It is quite literally impossible to have anything figured out for more than just a moment because in the next moment one of an infinite number of variables will have changed.

Stewardship work, therefore, is not now and never has been about "figuring out" nature or even agriculture. It's about figuring out ourselves and how we can put ourselves in the best possible position to react with humility and wisdom in the face of the unpredictable. We don't need farming to solve the ills of other industries or individual actions; that is too lofty a goal, and we have no evidence that it's achievable. We need farming to provide food, and sometimes fiber or fuel, in a way that doesn't fundamentally threaten our ability to inhabit our planet and doesn't impoverish the people who make it happen.

To develop the farms of the future, the necessary first step is to develop the farmers of the future. Despite our collective impressions around the jobs in agriculture, farming well demands significant skill, intimate geographic knowledge, and personal dedication. And as the climate, landscapes, and ecosystems of the world continue to undergo radical transition due to climate change, the demand for more people—that precious fertilizer that is a farmer's shadows—is only growing.

BASTA, ENOUGH

As Don Bustos of Santa Cruz Farms in New Mexico has gotten older, he's realized that one of the most important parts of his journey to farming well was understanding his limitations. Not just upper limits either, in terms of how much expertise he can gain and how much he is willing to sacrifice, but lower limits too: knowing how much money, work, and security is enough to fulfill his needs.

"Once you start to realize that 'This is what I want' and 'This is how much is enough,' then you tailor your life and your lifestyle to meet those demands. It's more about understanding your inner needs and being able to use that to come up with an actual farm plan and implement it, one that works financially and emotionally for the farmers and their families." So, he says, it's vital to really understand how much is enough in terms of the limits of natural resources, including those that are internal to the people involved.

This, from everything I've seen, is where good environmental outcomes really start. Not in the soil, the plants, or the vision. It starts when farmers honestly and genuinely decide how much is enough.

How much land, how much wealth, how much production, how much work, how many crops, how much sacrifice, how much attention, and how many accolades?

Within capitalism, contending with "enoughness" is anathema. It is unheard of. When challenged with how much is enough, we inevitably wonder:

How would anyone know how much is enough when the future is so uncertain?

Isn't it cowardice not to want to do more?

If I'm doing well, shouldn't I enlarge my impact for everyone's benefit?

Don't limited visions lead to limited outcomes? How am I supposed to land among the stars if I don't shoot for the moon?

If we're going to survive climate change, don't we need audacious goals? Couldn't it be me who does it—redefines agriculture, feeds the world, and saves us all?

Wouldn't it be better if I owned that land/sold that food/controlled that dollar than if it were someone else, someone less ambitious, less intelligent, less ethical, or less inspired?

Isn't it right to want to change the world?

Channeling my inner well of enoughness, these are my answers:

If you know yourself, you know the answer.

It is wisdom, not cowardice.

With greater reach comes greater demands and you are not infinite. It's better to leave room for others to have impact too.

You are not responsible for the whole vision. You belong on Earth.

The world does not need saving, and you alone do not have that power.

It is best for you to have what you need, so that others can have what they need too.

Our world existed before you and will exist long after you. If you want to change something in it, let it be yourself.

Internalizing these ideas is something I'm still learning, and it is hard. So much about modern American culture rejects these kinds of essential and honest limits. But if we want to create a food and farming system that leads to good environmental outcomes, this is where it starts. Answering these kinds of questions will undoubtedly require us to challenge some of the tenets we cling to when thinking about new farming methods. One brief but critical example: our attachment to focusing first on soil is undone by realizing that we must focus first on the people, because healthy soils in farm systems are tended by well-cared for humans.

Finding the answer to these kinds of questions is not something that we do once and then is done forever. It's a lifelong journey.

"It's not something that's going to be accomplished in a year, five years, twenty years," Don advised. "It's a lifetime achievement to be able to reach those goals. So I tell people it's good to make short-term plans, but then you have to really realize how much you need. That's the most important thing there is." And critically, he says, a farmer must build in that personal ethic at the start, not in the future. Otherwise, there's no other way to avoid destruction, from the degradation of the landscape to burnout.

Don came by this wisdom honestly, from his collective farming ancestors. His farm was named, in part, after a community established by sixteen families upon their settlement in the Española valley as part of the Santa Cruz de la Cañada land grant.

"The first thing they did is they built the *acequia* systems together with wooden shovels," he tells me. *Acequias* are earthen channels used for irrigation that are known as feats of engineering ingenuity and boons for natural systems, providing critical water and rare, vibrant habitats in parched landscapes. "The *Acequia del Llano* is seven miles long, and it's a windy little ditch, a way to transport water. And you can imagine families just getting together and working together to get water here and then up to these arid areas." For Don, these stories and memories, and the *acequia* itself, are at the heart of his work. We stood over it on that hot afternoon, clear, cool water flowing a few inches under our feet, looking for all the world like a common creek, living proof that human work is natural work.

"So to me," he says, "it's always been about community. The way my dad and my mom taught me is we're just here taking care of the land for a little while, and you better make sure you take care of it right so that when the next person comes along, they're taking care of it also." Don thinks the Western privatization of land and water resources, in his area in particular, was a huge mistake. "We're talking about water, a very limited resource, as a private right instead of a communal right. But all of the community should have access to healthy drinking water, healthy water for irrigating fields and for recreation." Don says he hopes the concept of private land ownership is challenged going forward.

"More communal ownership of land and natural resources should be an approach that benefits all communities," Don says, "because we're just caretakers of these resources." Don doesn't know precisely what that future holds—perhaps the expansion of the role of land trusts or public ownership. What he does know is that a tiny group of people owning a vast majority of the farmland while the masses yearn for land, for home, security and food, is not going to last forever. "At some point, we have to say *basta*. It's enough. We can't just let these one-percenters run the whole globe and force us into a system that's not viable for everybody."

PART 2

FARM YOU ALL

BIG TEAM FARM WISDOM

The first four chapters of this book aimed to offer a basic introduction to a big team farm's core priorities and how various farm businesses have been organized thoughtfully and creatively to work towards those goals.

The stories of these farm businesses illustrate that there is no secret sauce or silver bullet to building a successful big team farm. There are myriad strategies and, more importantly, countless opportunities for operations with different styles and systems to coexist. There are even opportunities for those farm organizations to build relationships with other farms, creating more synergies through cross-investment and finding more innovative ways to get good food to the people.

Food and farming are not easy businesses to get into, and the pressures of the space can be intense. But our craving for connection and meaning has opened a range of possibilities to start different conversations with consumers about food, environment, and human impact. Businesses are already forming, growing, and participating authentically in this conversation and reflecting their customers' values within their organizations.

Farm businesses that are not thinking about these priorities are already behind.

These big team farm entrepreneurs lead not by going it alone but by building coalitions, both within and outside their operations, of employees, colleagues, customers, and partners, to gain access to the skills, resources, and markets they need. None of these entrepreneurs built their farm business by relentlessly extracting from their people, by working themselves to the bone, or by undervaluing their customers' well-being or the health of their landscapes. They built successful farms by focusing on the people first and letting everything else come after.

The following five chapters offer some practical advice on how to start taking baby steps along the paths these businesses have traveled—for current and aspiring farmers, investors, policymakers, and the rest of us. Here, I'll do my best to distill wisdom that I've heard and learned from the fabulous community that populates this book and its predecessor.

A final note: The advice shared here may seem frustratingly vague. There are several reasons for that. One, the farm business leaders who contributed these insights are meaningfully diverse, with different goals, products, employees, strategies, and customers. I've done my best to capture the core principles that underlie their decision-making with the understanding that every entrepreneur and team will turn principles into practices in their own way.

Moreover, if there's one thing I know about farmers and entrepreneurs, it's that they hate being told what to do, especially by someone who hasn't done it themselves. Though these ideas do come from food and farm business veterans, I hazard that none of them would be interested in offering step-by-step advice in much detail, because they know better than anyone that the specifics of what worked for them likely will not work for others.

CHAPTER 5

In the Beginning of a Farm Business

———

Given how long and how deeply I've been involved with agriculture, I still surprise people sometimes by admitting that I don't really have an interest in starting a farm.

Though I certainly understand those who want to. I've spent the last decade being unsettled in what feels like every way—moving apartments, cities, states, or jobs at a pace of about once a year. Farming, whatever else it might be, offers the allure of stability and deep connection to place. I've often wondered what it would be like to have a space on Earth that could sustain my needs for a lifetime. What would it be like to be rooted to a geography, a career, a community, and a tradition? I don't have that answer.

For those of you who have gotten this far and still crave these answers more than you fear the difficulty of finding them, I commend you. Here's what I've learned about how to move, carefully and thoughtfully, down the road to starting a farm.

ARE YOU FARMING OR HOMESTEADING? BE HONEST

I get pushback for using the term "hobby farm" to describe homesteads because some argue it diminishes the level of work that goes into these projects. But the thing is, many hobbies take an exceptional amount of work, and describing them as hobbies does not diminish that fact.

I grew up on a hobby farm, and doing so, I learned a lot about entrepreneurship, life and death, responsibility, work ethic, and confidence. I would not discourage anyone from the desire to live or raise a family that way. But I think it's important to remember that choosing to live on a hobby farm or homestead is not the same as starting a business and should not be expected to automatically lead to income or returns, just as buying an easel and paints doesn't mean you are automatically deserving of gallery space.

Hobbies, by definition, are not about making a profit, and people pursuing their hobby are unlikely to prioritize creating good jobs, good food, and good environmental outcomes over, say, personal enjoyment or wealth accumulation. Buying land to farm for fun is a hobby that I believe people should have the freedom to pursue, as long as they can afford the true cost. I do not think, however, that these hobby farmers should be eligible for benefits—particularly tax benefits—that are ostensibly paid for by the public to further the public interest, not private ones.

For example, consider that agricultural property tax exemptions include hobby farms, rather than those properties being taxed at the same rate as other private residences (which is primarily what they are). That doesn't make sense alongside the acknowledgment of their hobby status. Similarly, a fishing boat might be a tax-deductible expense of a fishing business, but just because a yacht is a boat from which a line is sometimes cast does not mean it deserves the same treatment. I think if we more publicly and transparently acknowledged the difference between hobby farms and farm businesses, we'd see better outcomes in our farming systems, including more accessible farmland for people looking to farm for work rather than for fun.

In my research, I've also encountered many arguments that pitch homesteading as the keystone of a more just future for our food system. After all, the logic goes, if every individual family unit could just be responsible for their own nutritional needs, in effect, if we were all self-sufficient, that would be the best-case scenario.

For so many reasons, this argument is fundamentally silly. First of all, just about 1 percent of Americans participate in farming today, and most of those are in a highly mechanized type of agriculture that is not for personal consumption. Only a minuscule number of people have the skills necessary within their family unit to grow a complete or even partial diet. Not to mention that unless land were forcibly redistributed on a grand scale, the vast majority of Americans do not have access to the capital required to farm successfully, even just to feed themselves.

I've found little evidence to support even tamer arguments for the self-sufficiency of homesteads. Many have proposed anything from windowsill gardening to full-scale farms as ways to save money and gain access to better nutrition. There are certainly many intangible benefits to consuming food grown locally, but the reality is that most people with the free time, money, and security to grow food are most likely attempting to replace between 6 and 10 percent of their household budget—the amount spent, on average in the US, on food (USDA ERS, 2021). But to do that a homesteader still needs to buy equipment and seed, use resources like land and water, and invest a significant amount of time and labor. And in most of the country, unless you're planning to cut all nonnative species from your diet, you're still going to spend a significant portion of that 6 to 10 percent of income on things like sugar, coffee, tea, chocolate, seafood, dairy, and meats.

In short, it's nearly impossible to reach nutritional self-sufficiency at the family level, and even to get close would likely cost *more* than buying food, not less. Thus, homesteading is not a practical or accessible path forward for the vast majority of our food system, and better solutions will have to center interdependence instead.

Homesteading or hobby farming is a privilege, one only accessible to the relatively wealthy. To homestead or hobby farm is a choice, and making it does not create an entitlement to continue doing so without paying its associated costs, and surely does not create an entitlement to earn money from it. So if what you're doing is a hobby that you intend to do in your spare time without the expectation of income—from the market, the government, or anyone else—that's your choice. But making this choice should also involve grappling with taking on the title of one of America's most venerated and problematic myths—that of the small family farmer.

FORGET THE RETIREMENT PLAN

The idea of retiring to a farm is a popular one, and only becoming more so. The distance and disconnect we feel from physical labor, natural systems, and our food is almost certainly a driving force behind this desire. To be able, at the end of a long career, to spend your days gardening, cooking, and watching sunsets from the front porch is a beautiful dream. It promises security, self-sufficiency, and independence, as well as a connection with nature and a sense of pride in and love for your work.

But it fails spectacularly to capture what farming actually is.

First, this idea of farming as a retirement plan implies that farming is an easily acquired, or even entirely intuitive, skill. But the reality is that people spend their whole lives building knowledge and expertise around farm work. It's highly skilled labor that is usually tailored to specific geographies, soils, crops, livestock, and systems. It is also physically demanding. Even some of the purportedly easier jobs on the farm, like operating heavy equipment, require fast reflexes and clear thinking to avoid the dangers that make farm work one of the riskiest jobs in America.

Second, as we've discussed, this beautiful, picturesque farm will most likely need the support of significant off-farm income, particularly if you don't plan to do much marketing. And moreover, farming badly, even on a small scale, can still result in devastating damage to local landscapes.

In short, farming is not a good retirement plan. Farming well is hard work and running successful farm businesses that create good jobs and produce good food is even harder, not likely the kind of work you're fantasizing about doing in your twilight years.

It's worth taking a moment to interrogate this desire and why it's so appealing. It may feel like a harmless fantasy to hold out for yourself on tough days. But it is harmful because by preserving the agrarian fantasy we give it power. We perpetuate its near-supernatural and yet hollow virtues. And, on a personal level, we give ourselves an out to go on making unfulfilling choices in the present because one day the rural American dream will be ours.

But for the vast majority of us, there will never be a farm upstate. There is only our lives now, and the choices we make today.

FARM TO BE WITH PEOPLE, NOT TO BE ALONE

The Homestead Act captured white imaginations, I think, because it proposed that, in a world where so many felt unfairly dependent on and beholden to others, unwelcome and powerless in a country they perhaps didn't understand, there was a place to go and be self-sufficient, not to have to answer to anyone. The frontier land it offered represented freedom and opportunity.

The problem with this idea is still one we're grappling with in agriculture—that you can offer up all the stolen land in the world, but without enough people and skill to work it, we won't survive. This is the fundamental flaw of the rugged individualism fantasy in agriculture.

At the end of the day, no one farms alone.

Robert, the Southwest citrus grower, has some valuable insight on this phenomenon. One of the things that attracted him to agriculture was the prospect of working alone. But in reality, because he's avoided the commodity agriculture space, opting for better returns and margins in other markets, he's found he's continuously face-to-face with customers, partners, or workers.

"I don't even get to be my boss. It's, 'The customer's always right,' as opposed to commercial stuff where you might have a friendly but antagonistic relationship with your downstream partners." From Robert's perspective, this is just a fundamental truth about non-commodity agriculture: it's not work that can be done alone. And he thinks that's one of the reasons why some farmers resist the idea of working more closely with consumers, because it takes away some of that feeling of being independent and above reproach.

"There are a lot of people that are just really hesitant to do that stuff. And it's weird because they say, 'Oh, I really respect the fact that you're out there, engaging with consumers, one on one.' And on the flip side, they say, 'Yeah but you're not really farming though, because you're just standing around at the table and having conversations with people.'" This perspective is both overwhelmingly common and wrong-headed. Selling food is an integral part of a farm business, and thus farming.

The fantasy of lording over a piece of land, and thus all the plants, animals, and people on it, and farming only as you please, is a broken idea. That path is inevitably destructive. Nor do farmers have a right to grow whatever they want, however they want, and assume their customers will necessarily pay a good price for it. Only through close collaboration with people, organisms, and ecosystems can we hope to forge ahead. That's what a democratic food and farming system look like.

This is what it means to be a farmer, not to be separate and above or diminutive and below, but to be an integral part of a community, be it the community of an organization, of customers, or ecosystems. So before you take the leap and start farming, take some time to interrogate why you feel motivated to do so, because we humans are social animals and farming is not a good path to isolation.

DEFINE YOUR LIMITS, KNOW YOUR ENOUGH

Whether you're looking to bring on a new partner or hire employees (who are also potential co-owners in the long-term), a first step in the process should be for you, the owner, to complete an honest assessment of your personal skills. Taking this inventory should help you understand both your abilities and weaknesses, and as such will highlight what to look for in potential collaborators.

There are many methodologies and tools out there to help you carry out this assessment. I'm partial to the one found in Forrest Pritchard and Ellen Polishuk's book *Start Your Farm*. At the top of their skills assessment is business experience, notably accounting. Understanding how to effectively run the books for your farm business, determine pricing for your products, and evaluate the profitability of new opportunities are some of the most critical and underrated skills in farm businesses. Part and parcel of recognizing that farming in America is not a noble, independent pursuit where success can be achieved through pure grit is also recognizing that a farm business must be carefully and profitably run if you want it to survive. If you have no love of spreadsheets, QuickBooks, or number crunching, finding a partner or employee who does should be at the top of your list. And, just as importantly, you need to defer to their expertise and give that person the power to make and break your decisions based on what they know.

Beyond that come production capabilities: technical farming skills and know-how. Someone in the organization must have those skills, but they won't necessarily overlap in the same individual who has the business skills. The botanist-hydrologist, who is a wizard with the vegetables, likely won't be interested in spending time in the office or as a salesperson, nor would you want them to waste their valuable time that way. Everyone in the organization doesn't need to wear every hat all the time.

Marketing is another major skill set. How excited are you about selling food or fiber, building relationships in the community, and promoting and protecting the organization's reputation? These aptitudes are also fundamentally different from the others and may not overlap in the same person.

The final set of skills to assess comes under the general category of leadership. How excited are you about creating a team, helping build intra-organization relationships, cultivating individual careers, and overall guiding of the group? How inspired are you to create a near-term and long-term vision that not only motivates employees but also hypes up customers, media, and supporters too? If this isn't you, you'll want to find a stellar manager to fill the gap.

Once you have your arms around the full suite of skills that the farm business needs, you might be overwhelmed by the demands. How can one person contain or master each of those different competencies? Mostly, they can't. That's where the team comes in.

These are all vital roles that need to be filled in a big team farm. Even if you are the rare unicorn who feels confident about and excited to take on all these responsibilities, you should accept right now that if you want every one of these roles, there will be nothing left of you when you're done. No free time, no family time, not an ounce of yourself will be spared. I can't emphasize enough that performing even just one of these roles at a high level is exhausting. So be honest with yourself and acknowledge that your time, energy, and attention are not limitless resources. No amount of passion for your project will change that; faith isn't a substitute for rest. Determine which roles you will fill best, while permitting yourself to be a whole human, and determine how to fill the remaining positions with people you trust.

Finally, do the work that New Mexican farmer Don Bustos advised and think long and hard about what is enough for you. How much income, time, wealth, or security do you need to be content? What limits can you put in place such that you are encouraged (or, better yet, forced) to stop pushing for more when you attain your levels of enoughness? Don't wait to do this work—it's best to do it before you start farming—because it takes decades to master.

FIND AND GROW PARTNERS

To me this work is the heart and soul of real big team farms, and it's also difficult and painful. Meeting and building relationships with people is always hard, especially when it's people you want to do business with. Tending to and maintaining those relationships over time, through the obstacles of financial hardship, profound disagreements, and the incredible stress that often comes with farming, is even harder.

The best advice I've heard about finding partners is to do it early, before you buy land, before you set your heart on cultivating a specific animal or crop, and long before you quit your day job. Find people with whom you can build trust and with whom you can see yourself spending workdays that will often be long and grueling. It's critical to also find people who are genuinely different from you.

This isn't just a trite call for representation. The diversity of your team will directly correlate to the success of your business. People just like you, people who like the things you like and with whom you have overlapping experiences, are going to draw from the same well of solutions you do, reach the same customers, and be interested and impassioned by the same problems. A little redundancy can be good, but a lot is, well, redundant. To take full advantage of opportunities to reach new people, grow uncommon crops, and farm in ways better aligned with natural systems than ever before, and to have a fulfilling workplace, requires a diverse mix of people, not monoculture.

So go out there and look for partners. Practice your pitch. Craft a vision. Figure out what you have to offer others who dream of farming and being tied to the land, and flex your coalition-building muscles. If you don't have those muscles, farming might not be for you because that's exactly what farming is: building coalitions between partners and employees, between the farm business and its customers, between water, soil, nutrients, plants, and animals, not through force, manipulation, or deception but by finding a way, day after day, through tender care, for all to thrive.

People who historically have not had the power to bend others to their will through force tend to be more practiced at working collaboratively to gain consensus. Many groups have lacked this access and power in American agriculture: women, people of color, and LGBTQ+ people in particular. We need farm owners and leaders from all these groups, and we need them to be empowered to make decisions, communicate with communities they're a part of, and be present in our landscapes. Center these perspectives and treat these people as partners, not just in name but in every possible way. Give them power and resources proportional to their talent and contribution.

Then ensure that some of these partners are good at growing crops you all care about, others at marketing, some at sales, and some at logistics and operations. Make sure everyone understands why each job in the organization is important and ensure that everyone has the chance to build skills, evolve, and to build a career for themself. Cultivate connection and understanding among your partners.

This is the real work of being a farmer. Farming, at its core, is about supporting communities.

Finally, make things official. Engage a lawyer or similar professional to help you create formal partnership agreements. Discuss transparently what will happen if a relationship goes south. As Lance Woodbury advised, before you get into business with someone, figure out how you'll get out of business if you need to, including how you will split up the farm's assets and debts.

Formal employment agreements are also important. Ensure that your employees are clear about their roles and responsibilities before they agree to come on board, and be willing to revisit the formal document as their positions and the business evolve. For many interested in farming, the idea of a handshake agreement has an aesthetic appeal, but when people's livelihoods and housing depend on upholding agreements, handshakes are risky. It's better for everyone to have the indisputable clarity of a written contract, however unnecessary and laborious the process might seem, than for the farm owner or employee to end up in a sticky situation with no recourse.

OR BECOME A PARTNER, RATHER THAN A FOUNDER

Because of the social and cultural tea we're steeped in, the idea of being a founder, of starting a farm as the singular, visionary architect, is much more attractive than that of being the second employee, or the third or fourth. That is partly because entrepreneurship more broadly struggles with the same emotional mechanisms as farming—we tend towards idealization of icons, of believing in the myth of the lone entrepreneurial genius.

But how many of these rugged individual business leaders succeed, proportionally? The ratio of successes to failures is staggering.

When we take the time (and the hefty dose of humility) to acknowledge how few of us have the full range of skills needed to farm well, it becomes apparent that more people are required to do it right. As an aspiring farmer, the good news is that you don't necessarily have to start from scratch. You can determine your skills, be they in marketing or accounting, managing people or technology, agronomy or animal husbandry, and then reach out to existing networks in search of partners. Find people who have complementary skills to yours and communicate candidly about how you can work together, and what tangible and intangible resources you have to contribute.

A final word of advice—use caution when making life partners into farm partners. Family members and significant others can seem like ideal business partners because of already-established trust, social dependencies, and familiar communication styles. Anecdotally, I know many couples who have been torn apart by farming together. So choose your partners with care and build strong bonds with them, but realize that choosing to work with someone with whom you also share every other aspect of your life can be a risky proposition.

KNOW YOUR OPPORTUNITY FIRST

If you decide that you have the technical skills to farm and have found a few partners who can round out the organization's needs, then the next step is to identify your market opportunity. Finding the product or service that only you can provide will require market research, a healthy dose of creativity, and a lot of trial and error.

Start thinking about what unconventional markets might be out there. One potential market, the more obvious one, is on the food side—is there an opportunity to fill an under-served niche? Is there space for you to offer a familiar product at an unusual time, place, or price? Is there an opportunity to grow a market for an uncommon product?

Unfortunately, especially at the beginning, dialing in on a price that works for the business and for your customers is one of the most difficult challenges. The market for food is a competitive one, and it (and your future customers) have no sympathy for beginners. Know that despite all of the advocacy and "consumer education" that's gone on in the food space in recent decades, American consumers are still incredibly price conscious about food, and pointing out that farming is expensive or hard is usually not a convincing sales tactic. Your customers will more gladly purchase your products at the price you set because you have something no one else has and they've been looking for it.

Creative thinking about where to find possible revenue streams should extend to every part of the business. Especially as awareness about climate mitigation grows, there is exploding interest in paying land managers for ecosystem services. Remember Jack and Jenya's grazing business from Chapter 4? If your farm business offers excellent landscape management, there are certainly unconventional opportunities to market that service, whether to municipalities in need of fire suppression, private property owners looking to manage "wild" spaces for hunting and fishing, or even progressive ecological areas that recognize that human intervention is part of nearly every landscape on Earth. In other words, high-skill farming itself can be a revenue-generating opportunity.

The idea of being paid to farm by a landowner might seem far-fetched, but there are existing companies that offer this service, in a category called "farmland management services." Furthermore, there's a whole separate section of plant and ecosystem management grouped outside the farming space—landscaping—that involves this exact transaction: paying skilled workers to manage private property. It's not beyond the scope of imagining that this same mental model could extend to agricultural production when the right farm business and landowner are involved.

More to the point, management-intensive farming practices that increase the resiliency of soils and other natural systems add tangible value to agricultural land, often increasing their sale or rental value. This means that when tenant farmers use these practices while paying market rental rates, they're subsidizing the improvement of private land and generally need to pass on that cost to their customers. The landowner in this case is increasing the value of their property commensurate with healthier soil, streams, plants, and animals and, on top of that, collecting rent from a farmer who is paying them for the opportunity to do all the work. This scenario is untenable for a for-profit business and, without outside subsidization, is unlikely to be successful in the long-term.

Successful businesses identify an opportunity and begin building from there. This should come long before you consider buying farmland or other capital assets because you'll want to match these resources to your product and the market you serve.

THINK ABOUT GROWTH DIFFERENTLY

I've met a few farmers who are turning the idea of "get big or get out" on its head. And they're not doing it because a policy changed or because consumers suddenly "got educated." They're doing it because eternally figuring out how to grow more crops to buy more acres and on and on is not the vision they have for their farms or their communities.

Agriculture became obsessed with the idea of economies of scale long ago, and it's amazing how quickly we forgot that just because economies of scale exist doesn't mean they are the only way to make a business successful. That's a good thing too: if the only way to grow a farm business was to grow more cheap raw products than the incumbents, new and beginning farmers wouldn't have a chance.

The only reason "growth" on a farm means adding acres or increasing yields is because we allow it. Businesses can grow in many directions, and great businesses grow in many directions at once. Growth comes from your partners and employees getting more skilled and creative; it can come from new business lines that add value to raw commodities while thrilling your customers and it can come from more purposeful management of resources that may seem external to the business. For example, you could sell hunting leases in your well-managed forests, offer tourism venues or event space on beautifully maintained meadowland, or collaborate with nonprofits or federal agencies to do habitat restoration and earn conservation dollars, maximizing the resources you have available from multiple angles.

Getting creative with possible income streams is something that new entrants do very well compared to the old guard. Don't leave your comparative advantage on the table. If good jobs, good food, and good land tending are your goals, your farm's growth path will not be one dimensional. And it might even mean that expanding the organization means a smaller geographic footprint.

BUILD A RELATIONSHIP WITH THE LAND

When working in collaboration with natural systems, there's no such thing as a hard and fast rule. Your landscape, resources, and goals are unique and will require advanced customization and continuous adjustment.

For this reason, a critical role for land managers in your organization will be to sort through all the noise around farming "sustainably," "regeneratively," "ecologically," or even "biodynamically." They will need to sift out the relevant wisdom for your context and discard the rest. As the climate continues to change more rapidly than it has within living memory, gaining knowledge about best practices from a wider world of farming practitioners is essential. At the same time, a grounded vision and detailed understanding of your operation's unique context is the only thing that will help your farm avoid wasting time and resources chasing every new trend the alternative food and farming world churns out.

Building a relationship with your specific landscape also means working to avoid complacency when utilizing heritage practices. We cannot laud the past and tradition for its own sake; we have to practice and evaluate methods with a discerning eye to determine whether they serve us, and, in the same way, whether modern science and technology offer value.

Your land management ethic will surely face outside pressure, whether you're dealing with tutting neighbors or snide remarks at the gas station, raised eyebrows from your trendiest customers, or dismissive notes from purist, would-be supporters. Farming well isn't clean or pretty and it doesn't always look nice from the road. It's almost never uniform, and it's difficult to do it well if you're focused on checking boxes and passing third-party audits. The heart of good farming lies in collaborating with people, land, and animals in a mutually beneficial way, and that work should be resistant to fads and buzzwords.

The reality is many of the practices we've used in the past, and remain infatuated with today, are just different flavors of the same old desire to force a simplistic, toxic order on a world that doesn't need it—a world that thrives on a holistic and elegant design beyond our control and comprehension.

Procuring food, fuel, and fulfillment within natural systems requires the humility to accept that the chaos we perceive in our landscapes is a product of our limited understanding of complexity, not a flaw in its construction. Some will surely say it is easier, better, or more correct to wring nutrients from an unwilling landscape by force. There is undoubtedly a connection between a long history of Americans holding the land hostage to our needs and the toxically masculine pride, independence, and self-assuredness we associate with those who plow "virgin" soil.

You cannot have that kind of relationship with the landscape you depend on and honestly claim to farm it well. The ethic that you and your team agree on should reflect your interpersonal agreements and be grounded in mutual respect, not force and coercion. And in many cases, when farm businesses take the time to think about the landscape first, they find much more creative ways to utilize the energy of the earth to help them reach their goals. Think of Jack and Jenya and the way their grazing business has helped them raise their sheep such that they collaborate with a sensitive environment and provide a financial return to the farm. This allows them to look beyond the false American farming imperative to always grow the most stuff no matter what.

THE CAPITALISM IN THE ROOM

You might do everything right, follow all the advice you've heard in this book and beyond its pages from mentors and friends, and it still might not work. Your big team farm might still fall apart or never come together at all.

There's a good chance this is because of that old standby: capitalism. The majority of American cultures have been worshipping at the altar of capitalism for so long that the average person may not be in a position to understand the value and possibilities of collectivism, the avoidance of extraction, or the very idea of having enough.

In doing this work, you'll find customers, employees, partners, friends, and other supporters who think your attachment to these principles is silly, naive, defeatist, or even destructive. When selling products at a price that covers its total cost of production, you'll have customers accuse you of gouging. When creating plans and building infrastructure, you'll have partners and employees who want to go bigger, grow more, and accumulate more power and wealth than you or they identified as enough. You'll have supporters, fans, and backers who want you to take over more land, expand, raise money, and gain accolades and celebrity as a testament to their own ingenuity.

It will be up to you and your team to stick to your prices, to control the team's individualistic impulses with collaboration and consensus, and to learn to hold your boundaries and keep your focus against the extractive impulse of our economic system which thrives on breaking everything down into discrete units with price tags. This work alone is exhausting, and you and your team will have to do it in addition to growing and running a food business and maintaining your relationships with one another and the land.

If this sounds nearly impossible to you, I wholeheartedly agree.

CHAPTER 6

In the Thick of a Farm Business

If you're currently farming and you've gotten this far, bless you. I'm positive that a lot of what has been discussed so far has been discouraging, unwelcome, or straight up annoying, especially coming from someone who is not a working farmer. I get it. Interrogating big life decisions and reconstructing mental infrastructure is *painful* work; it takes a long time and a lot of practice.

The good news is, if anything so far has inspired you, changed your heart or mind, or made you want to start thinking about things differently, this chapter is for you.

DON'T FARM YOURSELF

The bottom line is, the number one reason businesses fail is because they don't make a profit.

When it comes to selling food, many people, especially the most generous and principled, can get a little squeamish about making a profit. I know many farmers who get to the end of a long, hard year and, when they look back at the books, realize they just barely broke even or even lost money. Many find comfort in the excuse that it would be wrong to make money off selling something people need to live.

I'm not unsympathetic to that line of thought. The problem is, if your business is not turning a profit, then you're inevitably leaving it vulnerable to any number of possible disruptions that could lead to its collapse. And even if you manage to avoid failure it won't be because of the merits of the business; more likely, it'll be because you and your team made extraordinary sacrifices and put in extra hours and other resources for which you won't see any return.

However much we may begrudge it—and should fight to reform or overthrow it—we live in a capitalist society. If you don't charge your customers more than the true cost you paid to produce your products, someone else is going to pay for it. It could be you or your workers getting underpaid, overworked, and under-protected. It could be your customers getting subpar products. It could be the landscape you extracted from or otherwise damaged when you had to cut corners to stay in business.

The piper gets paid regardless. By ensuring that the farm business makes at least a meager profit—*enough* profit to sustain you and your team—you can ensure the people who can afford to pay the real price are asked to do so, and they are not allowed to push the cost onto the vulnerable.

Remember, you don't have to sell $50 packs of strawberries to do this, either. There is opportunity in the US today to sell fresh and value-added foods at a profit—it just requires finding the right people, the right product, the right place and time, and the right price. Don Bustos makes a profit selling squash for $0.89 a pound, and his customers thank him for it.

Find your squash.

DON'T BE A DICK(TATOR)

If you're interested in transitioning from a one person show to a team-focused organization, one of the first ideas you'll have to reckon with is understanding that teams don't have dictators.

Farming as an industry seems to have a particular problem with dictatorial managers. Perhaps it's because of the psychology of farming, which has long been about exerting control as a benevolent despot over a patch of dirt. Perhaps it's because it attracts people who ascribe to the idea that since there's no office, there will be no managers looking over shoulders, no associates to train, and no colleagues to negotiate with. For many, the allure of farming is the isolation and independence. In too many cases, when farmers find they need help after all, they end up begrudging their employees not only their failures but also their very presence—the fact that needing them creates need for management, training, and negotiation, which many farmers simply don't want to do.

The truth is that, despite the lore, those promises of independence and control were vastly oversold if a farm operates on a commercial scale. Farming well is about relinquishing control, being responsive and resilient, and being flexible in practices and plans. Farming well is not about a world without bosses because every customer you meet, sell to, or piss off is your boss, and, if you're lucky, you'll get new ones every day. Farming is not about being separate, apart, or above anyone else, making decisions from on high. It's about being down in the mud and muck, often overwhelmed by the sheer magnitude of the challenge you've taken on, and doing it together.

The only thing that makes it all bearable is not doing it alone. And if you want people to stick around, do good work, and take ownership of their role in the organization, you must provide good training and meaningful distribution of power. People, especially good people, won't stand a tyrant for long when there are other options available. So it's best to start accepting input from all sides as early as you can, flex those consensus-building muscles, and get on with it.

Practically, there are many ways to democratize food and farm businesses. Morning Star did it by empowering employees with self-management. Patrick at Harris-Robinette refused to let his people be meatpackers and instead trains artisans, treating and paying them accordingly. The Abundant Table, a Southern California farm we met in *Farm (and Other F Words)* operates through committee and collaboration, and their executive director leads by obeying. There's no right way to share power in a farm or food business. There's just the way that's right for your team.

Remember what Ari Weinzweig says about an empowering business: It's not that they have no problems; the difference is these organizations deal with problems in empowering ways. When you inevitably get frustrated, angry, or hurt by the people on your team, don't take it as a sign of failure on your part or malice on theirs. People are complex. Aim to learn and grow through mutual hardship. Deal with conflict early and thoroughly and establish clear and accessible pathways for your team members to handle problems as they arise. Don't be afraid to make things formal. Clear and consistent policies and agreements are the province of every successful business, and the nature of food and farm work does not make it an exception. Write down your principles and make them binding.

As part of this work, identify key advisors whom you trust and respect who will sit outside of your business. Formalize a board if you're comfortable with it. This well-rounded group will help advise you and your team through rough patches and to capitalize on opportunities. They can also help you stay grounded and can be a good source of advocacy and investment.

FARM WITH YOUR BRAIN

Ricardo Salvador of the Union of Concerned Scientists said it best when he described what should be the most valuable input to any farming operation—brain power.

"If you're managing because of your knowledge of, say, what it takes to keep microbes in your soil healthy, then you get this very fertile soil that you're not paying for." That means, he says, when you sell your produce "you're seeing a return to your management knowledge, skill, and ability rather than to just the capital that you're investing."

Though this style of farming is absolutely more difficult than the kind of extractive farming that's common in the US today, it also prods farmers to build the skills that can lead to a career in landscape management, within agriculture, or elsewhere. This kind of understanding, that a system can be shaped without being destroyed, requires careful observation, conscious thought, and devoted practice. It's nothing this book, a college course, or a childhood growing up in farming can teach. This understanding can only be learned with intention and long effort in a specific place and time.

This certainly applies if your contribution to the farm will be the technical skills of production and landscape management, but it also applies in every other part of the business. If you're taking commodity crops to the local elevator or packer, for example, you're technically "marketing" your product. But you're both leaving money on the table, by failing to seek a premium over the commodity price (which hovers around the cost of production, leaving little margin), and you're failing to capitalize on the intangible benefits of growing yourself as a marketer and salesperson. Building those skills is a challenge, but by doing so you can create the personal security of knowing if you ever decide to leave agriculture, you'll have developed professional capacities that apply in many other sectors.

It is possible in the twenty-first century to farm without your brain. The alternative is to farm with money—you can buy expensive inputs and fancy equipment, costly land, high-tech seeds, and hourly workers to do whatever tasks remain. This strategy has left many farmers, especially commodity grain farmers, as little more than heavy equipment operators and landowners. Their main contribution to their own business is to drive the planter, sprayer, or combine, depending on the season. Following this path leads to high human and environmental costs.

Assuming that you're not part of the tiny group of Americans whose money makes money, farming with your brain, and creating a return from your skills, is the more viable choice. Develop and professionalize your abilities and those of your employees as much as you can. They are what really makes money on the farm.

DON'T GROW COMMODITIES

I got the chance recently to talk to a Midwestern grain farmer who invested in an ethanol plant in the mid-2000s. As our conversation wound down, I asked him whether he's thought about growing more value-added crops at any point in his career. His response was to scoff, saying he's heard about value-added products and getting more for his grain his whole life, but the reality is farmers, himself included, want to grow commodities.

"We don't want to deal with marketing or customers, and it doesn't matter if the guy at the elevator hates my guts. If I take corn down there, he buys it. That's the way we like it." I've spent a lot of time thinking about this idea because what this statement fails to acknowledge is, in this kind of system, the only way to stay competitive is to grow more, cheaper crops all the time.

Here's why. A farmer with a few hundred acres of commodity corn is a tiny player in a huge market, taking prices that are set not by their own business but by its biggest and most efficient competitors. A good comparison might be a small-town diner selling $1 hamburgers because McDonald's does the same. The difference is, multinational fast-food giants can make a profit from a $1 hamburger and a local diner likely cannot. However, it's clear that the diner isn't doomed; the decision-makers there have other options. They could do things that a global fast-food chain can't, like find creative ways to customize their menu to the community's wants or offering unique options that aren't available at the local drive-through.

The same is true in agriculture—farmers can always fork over the proverbial $1 burger of commodity crops and take their chances at making a profit, or they can think critically about what they can do that no one else can, given their unique circumstances, and focus on expanding those capacities.

Many farmers, reading this at the end of a twelve- or eighteen-hour day are probably saying, "Like I have time for that. I already give up enough of my life to work." And you know what? You're absolutely right.

That's why you have a team. Hire a young, spunky entrepreneur to build you a product and a brand. "I don't have money to pay them," you say? Well, you've got land, don't you? Or a brand? A customer base and semipredictable revenue? Make them a partner. Let them work their way into owning part of your business. Then the incentives will be there not just to grow the business for your sake but also for their own.

Just so you know, #2 dent corn isn't the only commodity in the US. If you're growing something that can be cheaply or ubiquitously found at your average grocery store—from carrots to eggs to popcorn—those are commodities too. If you're trying to determine whether growing something is a market opportunity for your farm, ask yourself these questions:

- Are you able to sell your product cheaper or is your product better (tastier, more nutritious, etc.) than any other available option your customer can access?
- Are you growing at a time or selling your product in a place where no one else does?
- Are you growing your product better than anyone else, *and* can you translate that into a price premium?

If you can't say yes to one of these questions, then you may well find yourself in a place no farmer wants to be: trying to convince customers to buy something that they think is overpriced. Better to grow something only you can grow than wind up struggling against the ever-downward spiral of price competition in a commodity market.

FARM AT THE SCALE THAT MAKES SENSE

The idea that the only good farms are small farms is well past its best-by date. Just like everything else, good farm and food businesses can exist at many sizes and scales.

Operating at a larger scale than what many consider "small" is, in some cases, vital. If we want farm businesses to grow and sell healthy, nutritious food we likely need them to operate at a scale large enough to accommodate a full-time food health and safety professional, who can ensure tools and facilities are clean and procedures are in place to prevent contamination. Farms are dirty places, and that's okay, but we can't leave the safety of the food we eat up to relatively unregulated farms (and generally the smaller the farm, the less regulated they are), especially as disease- and pathogen-related risks increase with climate change.

If we want farm businesses to be able to think, plan, and farm in the context of a whole landscape, being mindful of watersheds, adjacent non-farmland, and vast habitats, there are clear benefits to having fewer, larger organizations. These bigger businesses can hire and coordinate bigger teams who can manage at the scale on which ecosystems operate. This is likely to lead to a better result than having countless minuscule and independently operated farms, making uncoordinated decisions based on personal preferences and limited to a few acres.

And if we want farm businesses to be places where people can find interesting, secure work for dignified pay, farms will need to be diversified enough that if a single crop or business line suffers a bad year it won't sink the entire operation. Diversification requires varied skills and competencies and some level of internal redundancy to minimize risks. Small farms struggle immensely to diversify in this way. Bigger farms usually do this better, and thus experience more stability.

Small may be beautiful, but small is not better. Small is not the most moral size; it is just a size. Find the right size for your team, limitations, and collective vision.

FIGHT CLEAN FIELDS

As someone who didn't grow up in the Midwest, I learned about the idea of "clean fields" secondhand, rather than how I imagine Midwestern kids do—that is, by hearing Dad or Grandpa say, every time they drove past a field containing anything other than tilled dirt, "What a mess."

The love of clean fields is still bizarre to me. It's not even pretending to be about anything other than aesthetic. It's simply the idea that farmers and neighbors prefer to see a field entirely free of any plants other than the ones that humans sow. Although it seems frivolous, the desire for this aesthetic creates resistance to better farming practices because alternatively managed fields, like those planted to cover crops, look messy. Plowed fields look nicer, the thought goes, uniform, empty. Nature conquered.

"There's a lot of pressure to not have any weeds in your fields," one farmer told me, "There's a lot of pressure to follow what the neighbors are doing [...]. It's a conformity thing." Conservatism verging on complacency and the idea of "doing things like Dad did" runs deep in farming. Sometimes with good reason, because someone in the past tried to change things once and it didn't go well. But too often, it has more to do with self-consciousness: *What will the neighbors think; that I'm weird? Crazy? Too big for my britches?*" This fear perpetuates the status quo, and much of American farming continues with tradition for tradition's sake.

The thing is, neither aesthetics, peer pressure, nor inertia are good reasons to choose practices that are neither economically nor environmentally sound. We don't allow school children to use the excuse that "everyone else is doing it" to explain their mistakes, so why would we let adults with agency and resources get away with such flimsy reasoning behind choices that have serious repercussions? We must stop centering and bowing to these childish justifications, and associated feelings, in our work around holding farms accountable.

FIGHT FOR REGULATION

This is an easy one if you currently farm well or are planning to. If you're running a smart, productive farm business and pursuing financial return to your team's managerial skills and marketing acumen rather than maximizing yield, it is in your best interest to fight for stronger environmental and labor regulations in agriculture.

See, if you're farming well—if your partners and employees are not exploited and feel like they have the power to make changes in the organization, if you prioritize your customer's health, safety, and happiness, and if good land stewardship is built into your business—you have nothing to fear from regulation.

"We're drowning in paperwork and bureaucracy from all these rules," is a common complaint among farmers. But, as long as there are no loopholes or exceptions, all your competitors will face the same regulatory hurdles. It will be baked into the cost of all the products on the market, even if you have to hire someone to keep your paperwork in order. And the benefits? There are the obvious ones of living in a safer, cleaner, healthier world, but there are also specific benefits to your business. Your corner-cutting neighbors who spray chemicals that damage your fields—they'll be regulated. The CAFO operator in the next county whose animal waste has poisoned the groundwater—they'll be regulated. And the person who undercuts your prices in the market because their meat is processed in unsanitary conditions will be regulated too.

Regulations are often neutral or even beneficial for farmers who already follow the rules. Fighting against regulation protects bad actors and bad farmers and hurts your customers and your community. Don't accommodate inaction or complacency.

DISMISS DOGMA

Remember that there is no exactly right way to start or grow a farm.

We've met farmers big and small, for-profit and nonprofit, raising livestock and growing plants as sole proprietors and as teams. And some of the philosophies, styles, and personalities captured in these examples might even seem to run counter to my argument that farms can (and should) operate as big team farm businesses.

I'll channel my inner Randy Woodley here and say that all dichotomies are false. The idea that there's one correct answer, one right way to farm or to build a successful business, is flawed. I fully expect there will be countless models, countless farms and businesses, and countless whole and partial solutions that help us get to a more resilient future with better food, better jobs, and better environmental stewardship. It's likely that not one of us is ever going to do it perfectly. Collaborating with nature to feed people is no place for dogma or hard and fast rules: it's a place for strong convictions, certainly, but also for the humility to hold them loosely. Prepare to learn, be proven wrong, and evolve and adapt often.

DON'T GAMBLE WITH YOUR FUTURE (OR OURS)

I once met a farmer in the lobby of a motel in Sioux Falls, South Dakota. I asked him what he did as we waited in line for coffee. With a wry smile, he confessed that he was a gambler. Perhaps sensing my confusion, his wife came up behind him and added that he's a farmer. Before they both walked away, I heard her say, "Our lives would probably be better if you were a gambler."

I watched my parents play that hand; watched them stress and strain about money and weather and livestock, struggling through pain, regret, and sacrifice. I knew that the farm was a great place to be a kid, but a hellish place to be a grown-up.

I've heard many people joke that farming is an addiction akin to gambling, and I've heard it said enough that you need to win the lottery to farm that I've worried about the connection people see between the two.

Farming as an independent operator certainly bears some similarities to high-stakes gambling. It is often sufficiently random. There's a minute chance of hitting the jackpot, so to say, of making money and "earning freedom," and a much larger chance of ending up broke. Every project, every investment, and every hour spent farming is one more coin in the slot machine or card on the table. And I think many spouses of farmers will be familiar with the idea that for most diehards the best years aren't when you cash out; the best years are when farmers double down, planning to expand even more.

Many reading this will say that's the nature of entrepreneurship in any field, and there's truth to that too. But far fewer people work full-time jobs to support their small-town bakery or bespoke accounting firm. Unlike most other industries, farming, as a fantasy, gets under people's skin. There's an illusion of a jackpot out there that will allow for the establishment of a retreat from the world, a kingdom where you answer to no one, where you and yours will always be safe to live as you please.

But, as far as I know, no state currently accepts freedom as legal tender. A farmer, at least, will always have to have money. If your farm needs to make that money, you'll need to sell something—land, produce, timber, or services. And if you have to sell something you'll need customers and good relationships with them to boot. In other words, the freedom from society that we associate with farm life dissolves as soon as your feet touch the ground.

Farming fantasies appeal to many of us because they are about being beyond society's reach. But community is what defines us as humans. Not having to account for anyone else's needs is not a human ideal; it's antisocial and, on a farm, perhaps even more destructive than in any other business where the ecosystem of workers, customers, and landscapes depend on each other to succeed. The farmer is not the center of the food conversation. The community is.

All this to say, if you want to be a farmer to drive tractors, the construction industry will pay you well to operate heavy machinery. If you want to be a farmer to hang out with cute animals, think about a volunteer gig at the zoo or the local animal shelter. If you want to farm to commune with nature, maybe a job with the National Parks Service or as a game warden would be a better fit. And if you're farming to live out a personal daydream, because of some vaunted idea about self-reliance, independence, and being king of everything the light touches, maybe buy a lottery ticket instead.

But if you want to farm because you care about people, plants, animals, and natural systems, and you don't mind hard work—some of it physical but most of it mental, emotional, and social—then you might want to farm. If you are open-minded and want to be challenged, if you're curious and love to learn, if you're motivated to be a good ancestor and descendant, by the measure of healing and not owning, then you might want to farm. And if you are excited about building a business, managing teams, cultivating relationships, threading the needle to grow food that's healthy for people and the environment, and then finding novel ways to get it to the people, then you might want to farm. If, more than anything, you find meaning in reaffirming the sacredness of people, land, food, and our world, then farming might just be right for you.

CHAPTER 7

Investing in Big Team Farms

———

Investing in regenerative farming is hot right now. Whether you're an individual with some extra funds looking to support a cool project in your community, a nonprofit or foundation looking for catalytic capital opportunities, or a major venture fund eyeing the intersection of climate and agriculture, people are looking to put their money where their mouths are in terms of making change.

I'll note for posterity that when I use the words "investor" or "investing" I am using it in the most general and generic sense. When we give money to a business in exchange for products, a stake in the company, social benefits, or even just prestige, we are investing in their success. This chapter offers advice on how to evaluate opportunities to put money and other resources into the food and farm system, no matter how much money you're working with.

FIRST, LAND BACK

First and foremost, the dangerously lopsided accumulation of wealth at the top of the food and farm system is not healthy for anyone, not least because "unearned wealth brings out the worst in everybody" (Phipps, 2022). There are countless ways that intergenerational wealth and power contribute to poor outcomes in our current system—from multigenerational land transitions that concentrate resources in the hands of people with no incentive to be good farmers, to family foundations with billion-dollar endowments funding token pet projects of board members, who are often disconnected from the realities of the people and places they claim to want to help.

In a more democratized food system, wealth distribution, especially as measured in land, water, and other critical natural resources, must be determined according to some other factor then lineage. Therefore, it bears saying, if high-net-worth individuals and organizations truly intend to have a positive impact on this sector, the most effective and important thing they can do is invest in shrinking the wealth gap.

Notably, this work extends well beyond the world of farms and food into the realms of wages, health care, housing, and more. Though funders may be excited about investing in "grassroots" projects in the countryside, food and farming are, in reality, intersectional with many other parts of people's lives, and therefore the shortcomings of agriculture and the food system can't be tackled in isolation. In short, social justice work is food system work, and vice versa, because the ag sector is not isolated. It does not stand alone.

Beyond advocating for practical measures that reduce wealth inequality, from universal basic income to tax reform, another way investors can address disparities in agriculture is to return land to groups from which it has been taken. This includes Indigenous tribes through the land back movement, and dispossessed Black, Asian, and Hispanic farmers who, at various points throughout US history, have been unlawfully and "lawfully" driven from land that was rightfully theirs, whether through physical violence and intimidation or insidious laws and policies.

Notably, this is not an edict to sell land to these people on credit, to lease or rent to them, or to purchase and hold it on their behalf. Land *access* is not enough; righting the injustice at the core of the American farm systems requires land sovereignty—in a word, ownership. This deep work is the most impactful way to contribute to a more equitable food and farming system going forward. Future farmers, farmworkers, their communities, and the environment are likely to benefit in both expected and unexpected ways from these foundational efforts.

Many in the investment community and beyond will find the idea of "free" distribution of productive land untenable. But we already have a long history of redistributing land and resources to people we profess will make "better use" of it: a vast swath of existing American farmland was given to the ancestors of its current owners for free or nearly free. Today, I think we could imagine a number of "better uses" for the nearly one hundred and eighty million acres that are in commodity corn and soybean production. Now is the time to act, and the investment community has plenty of land and financial wealth to help lead that charge.

LOOK FOR BIG TEAMS

A big team in a farm setting is rare, but there are few more evident indicators that a farm business has all the hallmarks of a worthy investment. The presence of a big team indicates its owners can think creatively about the risks and opportunities in farming, evaluate the value of labor, recruit and select employees that are right for the job, and have the interpersonal skills and leadership qualities to retain those employees. Certainly, not all existing big team farms are shining beacons of progress, but they're already bucking the toxic trend of radical, and often destructive, independence in farming culture.

Big team farm businesses with multiple partner-owners who are actively involved should get special consideration. These operations have diversified their risk and are more likely to make well-considered business decisions, as reaching consensus is likely a necessary part of the process. Plus, the operation is less likely to fall apart if one of the partners departs or even dies suddenly. Given that farm work is some of the US's most dangerous, it should give investors comfort to know that when multiple owners are involved, a catastrophe won't leave the work of running the business to an unprepared, ill-suited, or uninterested heir.

Employee-owned big team farmers should get even more special consideration, as the benefits of multiple owners are spread among a bigger group. And democratically controlled big team farms should receive this consideration as well, with self-managed farms like Morning Star—that don't have a hierarchical command-and-control structure—representing some of the most innovative and advanced of all. Like few other moments in history, the COVID-19 pandemic has revealed the deep problems with extremely hierarchical organizations in food and agriculture, where the vast majority of workers are considered low skill and have little power and few protections. Empowering employees with a management, if not an ownership, stake creates resiliency, redundancy, buy-in, and more just (and at times, even more lucrative) outcomes.

In short, big team farms are more likely than small family farms to emphasize the business's profitability over maintenance of private, familial wealth. Big team farms are more stable during transitions, are likely to make more rational economic decisions without factoring in personal and historical bias, are likely better able to attract and value the labor they need and are likely more capable of understanding the economic value of environmental stewardship. All of these qualities make big team farms an excellent opportunity for investors whose goal is to positively impact the food system.

EVALUATE FARMS LIKE BUSINESSES

In the last century, agriculture as a sector has been granted many exceptions which have caused significantly more harm than good.

Capitalism, especially the way it works in the current US context, leaves much to be desired, but one of its major theoretical benefits is the eventual eradication of bad actors by market forces. In other words, if you're bad at your job or running your business, you're not likely to last long in a competitive market. But the many policy exceptions we've made for agriculture have neutered this market mechanism. As any economist would predict, this bug in the system has led to many inefficiencies: the preservation and protection of bad farmers, the prevention of evolution and progress, and perverse incentives that allow too many farmers to degrade natural resources by growing products that aren't even in demand. And all while dodging standard tax rates, collecting direct federal subsidies, and avoiding nearly any oversight.

One entrepreneur I spoke with on this subject was direct about their experience working with farm businesses: "Most farmers and ranchers I work with do not know their profit margins; they do not make money, they do not make decisions based on profitability, or return on investment, or any project investment timelines. Honestly, a lot of them just get their tax break and they're happy. They're landed gentry, and their primary preoccupation is to hold on to the land asset, and the tax shield covers a multitude of sins for how poorly run the businesses are. So, the majority of businesses that I worked with were not profitable, and they should be out of business. Full stop." Whereas an average company and its leaders must answer to accountants, regulators, and a corporate board and investors, traditional family farms rarely have the oversight or professionalism to be held accountable for their decisions.

In my work with farmers, I've seen countless pieces of anecdotal evidence that this is indeed the case, and other key data points provide telling clues. Despite five years of declining net farm incomes between 2015 and 2019, agricultural businesses remained one of the most successful small business sectors with the lowest failure rates, suggesting that there's some other indicator of a farm's success (and dictator of its solvency) than its generated revenue (Mak, 2021).

As the entrepreneur told me, "I think many of them are content with this just being a lifestyle and trying to do it until they die. This is a life some choose because they're privileged to be able to choose it. And that means they often just don't want the additional stress of being an actual business owner and thinking about how they grow their business." This attitude is why farms and ranches neglect considerations that are routine in other industries: how they might capture new business opportunities, for instance, or whether an additional employee, be they a field hand or a salesperson, could be a net benefit rather than a cost.

There are many ways to evaluate the business and entrepreneurial acumen of a farm business team. For one, ask not only to see the books but also expect owners to know the value of both their own and their employees' contributions to the bottom line, and expect them to compensate accordingly.

Look at the market your potential investee plans to address. Determine how thoroughly they've evaluated the opportunity, its growth potential, and longevity. Ask farmers to elucidate their go-to market strategy clearly and require profit-and-loss forecasts. Expect that some of these market plays may have little to do with raw commodities and more to do with logistics, marketing, branding, and even processing foods. Expect farm business to take back control from intermediaries, orchestrate supply in novel ways, and provide more transparency to customers to earn more margin. A few more bushels of corn, tomatoes, or beef per acre are not a significant, unique, or defensible market opportunity in the vast majority of cases, but other opportunities that may seem tangential to farming (but truly are not) can be.

Agricultural investor Connie Bowen also advised that you evaluate how feasible it is for farms to actually access these markets, including the farm's capacity to plant, maintain, harvest, process, transport, and sell their products.

"Belief that there is demand is not proof that there is demand," she says, "and demand in a faraway city doesn't help if the product can't be shipped." Margins, she notes, tend to decline quickly when fresh and frozen shipping is involved, and working with a distributor is not always easy or affordable.

Digging deeper, she says, whether looking at crop budgets or business plans, is just a small part of a good due diligence process when it comes to farms. You'll also need to get out, look at fields and facilities, and, critically, talk to employees or partners, ideally in a setting where they can be honest and direct even if they have something to say that an owner or leader might disagree with. "Nothing kills a business more spectacularly," Connie says, "than dishonesty and misalignment at the top."

In short, do the same due diligence you'd want when investing in any small businesses or start-up. Don't fall for the hype, the public persona, or the tired excuse that farms are different from other businesses and should get to play by a different set of rules.

EXPECT FARMERS TO UNDERSTAND THEIR ASSETS

A significant amount of farmland in America is being actively degraded through soil loss, landscape degradation, and nutrient pollution. Not only can this have harmful impacts on adjacent land and communities, but it's also detrimental to a farm's bottom line because land and resource quality are linked to land's value and degrading it for short-term gain is a bad investment.

The instinct to elevate farm production goals over beneficial land management makes sense in the short-term because it's possible to monetize extractive practices through higher yields. This obsession with short-term gains intensifies when people approach retirement age, as is the case with the vast majority of America's farmers. But if a farmer realizes that the quality of the land is connected to its value, this approach makes no sense in the long-term. Maximizing yield while destroying a high-value land asset is poor management when it's possible to simultaneously optimize yield and ensure land assets appreciate.

This misunderstanding is part of the typical "land rich, cash poor" cliché in agriculture, which suggests that a farm family can own often extensive capital assets and still claim poverty. The reality is that these landowners are not poor at all—they're rich but illiquid, which isn't a good excuse for degrading landscapes. Lack of liquidity is not unique to farming, but is an issue across a spectrum of sectors, and is something to be managed by thoughtful business leaders, not side-stepped through outside cash infusions.

For a farm business to be worthy of investment, it must have leaders who understand every dimension and know not only how to manage cashflow but also how to leverage illiquid assets to the business's advantage. Farm business leaders should not be indiscriminately attached to the idea of owning as much land as possible, but should instead know how to evaluate the specific benefits and limitations of each parcel of land that the farm owns or controls.

REDEFINE SUCCESS

High-value food and agricultural markets already exist. Despite all that we've heard about the tyranny of the commodity market in agriculture, it is already possible for farm businesses to seek and find customers willing to pay more. It's just that in many cases farmers often lack the resources or motivation to do so. Many farmers would simply rather be in the field than marketing their products. Therefore, they opt for the easiest market to access, which will always be the commodity market. Some can't figure out how to marshal the time and money to do market research, spin up the processes to find new customers, do marketing, sales, logistics, and farm well. I agree that it's a breathtaking amount of work, which is why farmers should not be encouraged or incentivized to farm alone.

A key transition to look out for: when farm businesses find success in non-commodity markets, they often become food businesses, and so the story they tell about themselves might not center on farming at all. Vaughn Davis of School-House Farms is a prime example (and a farmer I've worked with in the past). Drawn by a love of birdwatching and a good friend asking him to grow birdseed on his farm, Vaughn started experimenting with turning commodity corn acres into something more valuable.

Although he had no experience in growing sunflowers, the main ingredient in most birdseed, he decided to experiment. So, he planted a couple of acres first. Then, through trial and error over the course of four years, reached well over three hundred acres. Birdseed was a good market for him, but he realized that he could also build his own oil press and sell direct-to-consumer sunflower oil too. Similar realizations also led him, around the same time, into selling higher value corn to distillers and popcorn-makers.

Today he sells dozens of products—raw and processed, wholesale and retail—shipping all over the country. His products feed birds, make beautiful bouquets, are distilled into fancy whiskeys, become snack bags of popcorn, and are even made into beautiful (and delicious) blue corn bread.

Vaughn isn't selling tomatoes at the farmers market or processing chickens in his backyard. He doesn't have an aesthetically rustic Instagram account to post regular updates from the field. Instead, he spends a significant amount of his time on sales calls, arranging logistics, exploring new market avenues, planning events, and working on product development. Neither SchoolHouse Farms nor Vaughn himself conforms very closely to the idyllic "American Gothic" farm that inhabits our public imagination, but he's running a solid farm business that would be an excellent opportunity for investment.

A final note in this vein on scale: When we think about solutions, in business, policy, and even nonprofit spaces, we are absolutely obsessed with the idea of scalable solutions. But it's worth pausing to think about how many of the fundamental issues we're dealing with, inside the food and farming system and without, are directly related to the fact that some past "solutions" grew to a far larger scale than is healthy or beneficial for our economy or society. We crave scalability as a sign of universal goodness, but the problem with that idea is that different people, places, and problems often don't call for a single "scalable" solution. They call for unique, customized, individual ideas that might only work in one very specific context. That's not a limitation! It's more likely a sign that a solution is real, durable, and resilient.

ENCOURAGE UNFAMILIAR BUSINESS MODELS

There is one well-trodden path in the traditional "How to Start a Farm" manual, and it boils down to: build skills, buy land, sell stuff.

The technology sector offers a different path. In particular, the modern software-as-a-service model outlines another way to conceive the relationship between farmer and land, and land steward and landowner. A small subset of businesses, in the ranching space in particular, have made strides in adopting something similar in agriculture.

"The best businesses that I've seen are professional services," says Christine Su, a former ag-tech start-up founder who's worked with thousands of ranchers in the course of her work. "They're usually founded and operated by people who don't own land and often by people who went to college and then came into ranching because they were interested in working outdoors. They took business courses, and then quickly realized the glaringly obvious thing that land is a capital expenditure, and you don't want to be in debt if you didn't inherit. So, they just provide grazing services to other landowners instead. It's a pure cash flow business."

The best and most professional grazing services, Christine says, make money from their knowledge. On one side of the business, these ranchers sign agreements with landowners who want their property grazed, maybe for tax benefits or for landscape management benefits like improved hunting. On the other side, they sign agreements with cattle feeders who need calves raised on the range until they're old enough to enter a feedlot. These ranchers don't own land and they don't own cattle; they just get paid to be the caretaker of both the land and the animals for either a set number of days or until the cattle gain a certain amount of weight.

"[These young ranchers] get to do what they love, they apply their skill set, and if they're really good then they get paid on weight gain. And they make the difference between in-weight and out-weight," Christine says. These contract grazing operations are more common among younger farmers, particularly those under forty. "It allows them to be nomadic and flexible. It allows them to get out of a contract, and out of toxic landlord or customer relationships, when it doesn't suit them. And it allows more physical and social mobility in a way that I think is very empowering."

This practice is also becoming more common in other parts of the world, Christine says. In New Zealand, young people practice a farming style in the dairy industry called "share-milking." The dairy owner, usually from the older generation, owns the infrastructure. The younger workers, or "share brokers," own some of the cows, and mix them together to make one big herd and then rent the infrastructure to house it. With a larger herd and more hands to manage it, the worker-owners can do much more in terms of advanced grazing management. At the same time, if the milk market takes a downturn, or if climatic conditions change, they can flex their herd size more easily and maintain more liquidity.

When considering the appetite in the US for this kind of business, Christine says it's probably more significant than you'd think.

"[The number of] absentee landowners are only growing in places like Colorado or Montana," she points out, "and when they come back, they usually want something to do, like hunting or fishing. And so, they want the streams to be running and the trees and brush to be clear. So, I know a fair number of contract grazers who actually just do ecosystem management for rich landowners. They either use grazing, or they'll do stream restoration or contouring, permaculture planting, etc., but you get paid a good amount of money to do that, especially if you take photos and show that you're managing the ecosystem." In other words, these ranchers are being paid to be landscape managers.

There are certainly limitations to this business model. In order to build a service around managing other people's land, these high-skill stewards sacrifice long-term land stability and the chance to build a settled community. They likely won't be able to add to or access the additional benefits that stability and community create for individuals and the business.

The dependence on relatively few wealthy landowners is also a risk in the short-term. The scarcity of clients concentrates the risk for professional land managers, and keeping those clients happy at all costs could get in the way of good land stewardship. In the medium and long-term, however, this model could allow stewards a stepping-stone towards transforming public lands into public commons, where ecological land management at the big team or even community level could displace what are currently private lease arrangements on public lands.

NONPROFIT FARMS DON'T FIX INJUSTICE

There is a place for nonprofit farms in the big team farm landscape, but let's take a closer look at The Abundant Table, a nonprofit farm based in Southern California, to understand why, in some cases, nonprofit models can be less than ideal. The Abundant Table is an employee-managed collective: though it empowers its members with decision-making power, the profits of their labor are funneled back into the organization and put toward their justice work.

This is a beautiful gift, and it's inspirational to see the ways communities find to empower themselves. But taking a step back, we should all be uncomfortable with the fact that this situation represents people with few resources—former migrant farmworkers—taking on both the effort and the expense of feeding marginalized communities. With all the public and philanthropic money in the world, I would think it's possible to help these communities gain access to the nutrition they need while also compensating these highly skilled farmers such that they might actually be able to retire one day after a long and physically demanding career.

The Abundant Table's justice work is critically important and should be compensated independently from their farming. I deeply respect their collective choice to pour the fruits (literal and financial) of their labor back into their community, but I believe it's possible to craft a more just food system where the most vulnerable are not the ones asked to make that investment.

In other cases, nonprofit farms can be downright unethical. Too many are financed and controlled by those who made their money extracting from people and landscapes, who then use nonprofit farms as part personal retreat, part tax shelter, and part strategy to greenwash their reputations. It is also not uncommon for nonprofit farms to emerge from the ashes of poorly executed for-profit farms, where becoming a teaching farm, retreat center, or similar boutique operation continues to provide the lifestyle and prestige benefits that so many crave, without any of the market accountability that (occasionally) keeps other farms more honest.

If you think that these kinds of farms must be essentially net neutral, you'd be wrong. Too many are poorly managed, leading to exploited workers and damaged landscapes, and often not even producing much food in the process.

Another flaw in the nonprofit model has to do with land-ownership. As we've explored extensively, one of the most important financial assets farm owners can leverage is the ownership or control of farmland itself. For farmers who would otherwise be paying rent, paying a mortgage on land allows them to build equity that can be leveraged to hire employees, make investments, and take advantage of market opportunities. Though many nonprofits making stable, low-rent land available are surely well-meaning, the bottom line is that rented land is not sovereign land.

UNDERSTAND THE INTERSECTION OF AGRICULTURE, CLIMATE CHANGE, AND TECHNOLOGY

Humans have done some amazing things with technology in farming. In fact, the size of the global population today can be directly tied to advances in agriculture, maybe even to a specific one: the discovery that chemical fertilizer can be distilled from the air (Hager, 2008). But too often we've accepted the benefits of technology, particularly the short-term ones, without considering the long-term ramifications.

This impulse is literally celebrated in high-tech spaces, captured by that Silicon Valley standby: "Move fast and break things." For decades, American agriculture has had a similar, and similarly problematic, catch phrase: "Grow more with less." We've built many tools to help us reach that goal, from the plow to the gin to the genetically modified seed. The problem is, just as moving fast and breaking things has left our society littered with broken things, growing more with less just led to a lot more stuff—more than we know what to do with. In fact, we've dug ourselves into a deep hole of overproduction, and we've tried to dig ourselves out by developing fancier shovels.

We've been chasing efficiency gains in agriculture for hundreds of years, and recently we've been told that investing in these efficiency gains (and the technologies that create them) is an investment in sustainability. The idea there is if we increase crop efficiency we will reduce pressure on land use, feeding more people while retiring more acres. Yet since the late 1800s, we've known that increased technological efficiency actually *increases* the use of resources, not the other way around.

Here's how this paradox plays out. Say I own one hundred acres of land—including fifty acres is good cropland that averages two hundred bushels of corn per acre. The other fifty acres are not as productive, averaging only one hundred bushels of corn per acre. Ten years ago, I needed to grow one hundred and fifty bushels per acre to make a profit, so I would leave my fifty less-productive acres fallow because, basically, the juice isn't worth the squeeze. This year, however, new technology is allowing me to grow three hundred bushels per acre on my good land and two hundred bushels per acre on my poorer land. Even assuming the price is about the same, that means I should now plow up and plant my fallow land because I could be making a profit on those acres too.

In this case, if it were true that increased efficiency led to less land in production, I should have been incentivized by the technological advances to plant only thirty-three acres to corn out of one hundred, because that would leave me with the same amount of corn as I was growing ten years ago, with less work. But, obviously, that's not how capitalism works! We would only actually expect people to make those reductions if supply was managed externally, like by the government, or if enlightened farm business owners had predetermined how much money they wanted to make and chose to forgo additional profit and income because they felt they already had enough.

In short, if you're investing to support a more equitable food system and curb agriculture's climate impact, investing in increased efficiency is only adding lighter fluid to our already-burning planet.

Even investment opportunities that profess to go beyond increasing efficiency can have serious limitations, especially when they involve either massive financial outlays to already-wealthy landowners or when they only make minor tweaks to existing extractive systems in an effort to make them "less bad."

In the first case, the "pay farmers for better outcomes" plan relies on the assumption that what's holding back investment in sustainable methods on the farm level is cash. Therefore, it assumes if we just supply the funds, farmers will be happy to adopt some climate-crisis-averting practices. Yet our experience with cover crops, which have languished for years with relatively low adoption despite the fact that USDA (and most states) will pay farmers to use them, suggests that farmers are responding to more than just economic incentives. In many cases, cost-share and even cash payments are not enough to encourage change, even when those changes accrue benefits to a farm's bottom line. Instead, much of this cash will inevitably flow to the biggest farms and empower them to get bigger.

In the second case, the idea that we can better our current agricultural system by inserting "regenerative" farming practices into conventional, mono-crop corn and soybean fields or confined animal feeding operations is, even at a first glance, total lunacy. The mind-sets, tools, and practices of an extractive system cannot be transformed by tinkering around the edges. Farming in collaboration with natural systems requires a serious and committed overhaul of our present system. There may be some marginal benefits to these cosmetic changes, but it's overwhelmingly clear that these small-time "opportunities" are more greenwashing than meaningful change.

NO FARMING WITHOUT PEOPLE

I asked Ricardo Salvador if he had any advice on revolutionizing the role of science and technology in agriculture. He began by pointing me towards the phenomenon demonstrated in an infamous John Deere YouTube video where a farmer harvests thousands of acres of corn from a control desk in his office—an either feared or anticipated future where farms are operated entirely remotely, like a video game (John Deere, 2013).

"[John Deere] imagines all of these things," Ricardo says, "and they see little space for people." Despite being a tech geek himself, Ricardo says it pulls him up short to consider this possible future because, in his eyes, the human contribution to farming is significant. "If it could all be boiled down to an algorithm, it would be a completely different conversation. But [farming] is both science and art. So, as a human activity, there are things that our economy doesn't measure, and that technology wouldn't replace. And we need to be able to make choices about the technology that we use and whether it's really serving ends that benefit us all."

To Ricardo, technology is a positive thing only when it's stacked up against the kind of world we want to live in and it contributes, rather than detracts, from that world. Taking this perspective requires us to ask questions about what is being replaced by technology, assess what those things, activities, and people mean to us, and consider that obsolescence isn't distributed at random. Someone is making those choices, and we need to think about who has the resources, power, and freedom to make them. Technology hides behind a veneer of impartiality but, of course, it's designed and implemented by people, with their inherent biases and fallibilities.

According to Ricardo, "Science is not neutral. We all want to know something. But if people who want to know something have money to cover the research that's required to do rigorous science—then [we should ask] what do they want to know? And why do they want to know it? And what use are they going to make of it? And are the people benefiting from that the same people that paid to generate that knowledge?" You can see, he points out, that there's a spectrum of answers to these questions that all lead to the fact that science is not neutral. And the same is true of the derivative of science: technology.

Though they likely didn't recognize it, the COVID-19 pandemic showed US consumers firsthand what it means when an industry puts technology first and people second in the food system.

Breakdowns in the meat processing supply chain left meat counters empty and prices soaring for many months. The shortage persisted because the US meat supply chain is extraordinarily brittle. It's built to extract every last drop of efficiency from every animal on the line, and every person who handles them too. This system is overleveraged on the side of productivity and concentration and failed utterly to plan for the kind of market disruption caused by COVID-19.

If the major meatpackers had thought carefully about the kind of risks that are only becoming more common as the planet warms, they might have realized that actions like investing in workers' health and safety and building plants at a smaller, more regional scale—although possibly costing an extra penny or two per pound of meat—would lead to a more resilient system that could adapt in times of crisis to save human and animal lives, feed people, and avoid waste.

"The present model clearly has failed," Ricardo said, "and exposed that it is vulnerable to these sorts of pinpoint dysfunctions that no one has ever thought of. The system needs to be reviewed so that it's not so vulnerable to one thing going wrong." COVID-19 is surely just the latest of what promises to be decades of further disruption to food production, processing, and logistics worldwide as global climate change accelerates.

What does that mean for the climate-conscious investor? Developments in technology that promise to squeeze the last ounce of "inefficiency" out of a farm or food process is unlikely to have the impact you want. Often, the inefficiencies technology seeks to eliminate are the well-being of a person, animal, plant, or landscape. These technologies won't stand the test of time either. The well-being of people, animals, plants, and landscapes is the measure of the resiliency of our sacred world. And resiliency is likely to be the key to surviving the next hundred years.

CHAPTER 8

Policy for the Big Team Future

———

When we talk about mechanisms for change in the American food or farming system, policy often takes center stage. Indeed, the federal government has done much to shape the farm sector over the last four hundred years, but the insidious roots of this country's agrarian mythmaking run deeper than, say, the bi-decadal Farm Bill. The reality is more complicated.

Of course, that doesn't mean there's no role for public policy or advocacy in building a more inclusive future for our food and farming system. It does mean, if we're aiming to make real and long-lasting change, we'll have to think more creatively and holistically and pay better attention to how policy actually works, rather than how we wish it would.

POLICY DOESN'T LEAD, IT FOLLOWS

As a starting point, we must reckon with how policymaking works in the US today. Our political systems currently privilege the preferences and demands of those with money and power, often over a vocal majority of less well-positioned players. Our political system is captured by entrenched actors—in agriculture and beyond.

Therefore, the idea that a critical mass of policy makers will one day lead the charge and rewrite the rules to empower those of us who are losing out in the current system, at the expense of the big winners, doesn't make sense. Though it may be morally right, it's not the way things work. For decades, our political system has shown that it would rather tag along behind economically dominant organizations, institutionalizing the status quo at their behest, rather than force change within sectors.

There is broader work, extending well beyond the field of agriculture, that could help shift this reality, like expanding voting rights protections, imposing term limits in Congress and the judiciary, and regulating the role money plays in political advertising and advocacy. But when we limit our gaze to the food and farming sector, I think the evidence is clear: if we want to change the way agriculture and food policy works, the first step is to offer an economically viable alternative to the status quo. Growing financially successful farm businesses, then, is a first step to reshaping policy.

For better or worse, it takes financial success—in short, money—to have a seat at the political table. Big team farms, owned and operated by farmer-workers, could gain the resources it takes to have a seat there, make changes even without the support of policy, and be well-positioned to guide future policy making toward rules more supportive of collaborative farming efforts.

Big team farms are, of course, currently at a political disadvantage in many ways, making it a challenge to go toe-to-toe with the existing players. The current political and economic rules are set up to advantage those who exploit and extract. Building an alternative within the system will not be easy. Still, it seems like a more viable path to change than the idea of someday marshaling enough political capital and courage to bring about radical new policy and hoping to build something better in the aftermath. Someday, I fear, will be too late.

THE FARM BILL WILL NOT SAVE US

The Farm Bill is a piece of legislation rewritten approximately every five years that codifies federal farm and food aid programs. Would-be food system change-makers have long targeted the Farm Bill as the source of all the wrong incentives in agriculture.

This attention is focused on the way the Farm Bill favors commodity grain production over any other type of farming, leaving subsidized risk management programs out of reach for other food producers. The answer, many advocates say, is to flip the equation around to subsidize fruit, vegetable, edible grain, and healthy meat production. Or, at the very least, minimize farm subsidies as much as possible and let markets encourage farmers to grow better food.

It is true that the federal government subsidizes American agriculture to the tune of more than $20 billion annually (USDA ERS, 2021). In the last five years, they've tacked on additional tens of billions more in an attempt to address a wide range of problems, from bad weather to trade deficits to COVID-19 (Zulauf, 2020). The farmers who received this tremendous infusion of cash have secured their political influence in the near-term: the money they've received will, in part, help pay for lobbyists who will push to expand existing Farm Bill spending. The idea that now, on the brink of the 2023 Farm Bill process, farmers and their advocates will be interested in changing the policies that have led to their enrichment is laughable.

The defenders of the current structure of the Farm Bill argue that these funds are an investment in national food security and provide the American public with the greatest abundance of cheap food on the planet. After all, they say, food is a basic necessity, and it should be affordable and accessible so that our communities do not go hungry. And yet tens of millions of Americans, including millions of children, remain hungry and food insecure. The trillions of dollars in outlays to our farming sector over recent decades have not had a meaningful impact on hunger levels in the US (Glauber, 2017). If those are indeed the aims of the Farm Bill's agricultural programs, they're doing an abysmal job.

So, what do we do with this behemoth of a farm system awash with federal funds that can't meet its one supposed goal of feeding Americans? If we look more deeply, we can see that the premise itself is faulty.

It's pretty much impossible to link the subsidy system in agriculture with food security in the US because farm policy was never about alleviating hunger. Farm policy has always been more about shoring up private property, encouraging the mechanization and consolidation of the ag industry, and placating a white, rural voting bloc whose interests have a disproportionately powerful grip on American politics (Daniel, 2013). No amount of reform is likely to reshape this system enough to contradict its original purpose and current function. Arguably, only eliminating the farm programs from the Farm Bill entirely would allow us to completely rethink farm policy. Otherwise, we're likely to waste our time simply shifting the advantages of an unjust system to a new group of beneficiaries.

The reality is the deep problems around natural resource extraction, labor exploitation, and wealth accumulation in our farming system predate the Farm Bill by hundreds of years. If we don't address the root of these issues head-on, they will live on, no matter what legislative reforms we put in place. Eradicating subsidies for commodity crops does not, in itself, incentivize farmers to create more dignified jobs, grow more and better food, or be better environmental stewards; because the Farm Bill incentive regime did not create the perverse incentives that reign in US farming, it just codified them.

I recognize that demanding the end of a policy rarely leads to its decline. A more meaningful strategy to change the Farm Bill would be to empower and support big team farms and other alternatives, helping them to grow into significant enough players to weaken the stranglehold of the conventional farm lobby and to lead the policy conversation that makes the most sense for them.

Not to mention, fighting against something you hate is never as effective as fighting for something you believe in.

HAVE THE COURAGE TO MAKE RULES, THEN ENFORCE THEM

A farm-sector investor captured a key sentiment that I heard echoed throughout my reporting for this book, "Everything buckles to the farmer. The farmer rules. Whatever the farmer wants, we give them in the end."

This amount of power, and our tendency toward capitulation, is not healthy. Yes, many farmers are good at farming, and some are even experts, but that should never mean they are above reproach or answering to their customers, partners, or regulators. A nation of citizens is a community and, especially in a nation where we spend billions of tax dollars annually in direct payments to farmers, the public should have a substantial say in how food is produced.

Markets, businesspeople, and industrialists are, in democratic theory at least, subordinate to the authority of the government, who is charged with acting on behalf of the public interest. That's the theory that ostensibly lays at the foundation of our democracy. That means policy makers and regulators have a duty to act for the benefit of the majority of us, not just for a small sector. And the public interest dictates that what we expect from farms (especially if farms need billions in taxpayer investment) is good food, good jobs, and good environmental outcomes. Holding farmers to those expectations or, at the very least, ending support for those who don't meet them should be the essential priority of our farm policy makers and regulators.

Regulation is absolutely a third-rail issue in agriculture. Farmers and their advocacy groups have been fighting new regulation for decades and have successfully evaded or undermined existing rules in the meantime. But the time is past for relenting to the demands of narrow-minded landowners who rack up costs that accrue to the public while they extract and exploit workers and our planet. The time is past for propping up farm businesses that refuse to act like businesses because of some imagined exceptionalism. Systems transformation requires an appreciation that change will likely disadvantage at least some, if not all, of the players who are advantaged in the current system. That's why making everyone happy is not the goal, but instead the aim of good policy is to provide everyone with as fair a chance as possible to pursue their own happiness.

Lawmakers will have an ally in this regulatory work in big team farms, who understand that formalizing rules they already follow, which require all their competitors to heed them as well, will only make their businesses more competitive, their land safer, and the country and planet more stable in the long run.

For those who aren't lawmakers, remember that it is within the power of the people in a democratic system to create the rules, the markets, and the rewards. We create the policies that make it possible for farmers and everybody in society to operate the way they do, not just through voting but also through the ideas that we discuss, take seriously, and treasure.

KNOW THAT FARMERS CAN TAKE REGULATION

Part of the reason regulation is such a controversial topic in agriculture is the perception that America's farms would disappear beneath the burden of following more rules. From what I've seen, that may be true for some farms, but for the farms that employ the most people, grow the most food, and occupy the most acres, that simply isn't the case.

Take, for example, EL-VI Farms in upstate New York. EL-VI is a two-thousand cow dairy with thirty-three hundred acres of cropland. The farm has around thirty full-time and another twenty-five or so part-time employees.

In 2020, I interviewed Kim Skellie, one of the partners at the dairy, about how the operation was planning to deal with the state's expanding labor rules which require overtime pay for farm workers after sixty hours a week, among other new protections. During my reporting on this issue, many farmers suggested these regulations constituted an existential threat; that these updated laws would put them out of business. Kim and EL-VI are not so troubled. They took the new requirements to their staff and negotiated how the team would work it out.

"They're probably averaging sixty-three hours a week, so they get some overtime. And that was the agreement. We want employees to stay here and be happy. And we didn't want to have turnover. So, we compromised." The farm has seen the fruits of that work: turnover has remained low despite the slight reduction in hours per employee. None of the workers fled to nearby states with fewer labor protections, as many of the rule's detractors predicted they would. In fact, the farm has hired an additional worker to pick up extra hours that others shed.

"I like to think that we're a preferred employer, so we tend to attract people [...]. We do have one neighbor farmer who has taken overtime [pay] to a higher level, meaning their people are getting really well compensated [...]. And that may cause the rest of us to raise the bar also." Kim says this with a shrug. He's not concerned about the dairy's ability to comply with these regulations or to compete with other employers.

Another new provision in the law establishes requirements that farms carry worker's compensation and unemployment insurance, which EL-VI has already had for decades. Injuries are a major concern on dairies, and in recent years the operation has been doing more around safety training for all employees. The professionalization that was required for the business to become bigger and more mature meant that little changed to meet the new regulations.

I probed deeper about the new protections for collective organizing. And Kim was again not too concerned, "I just try hard to have a staff that feels they can bring up issues and get them resolved and feel well enough compensated, so we don't get that threat. I worry about good teamwork and motivation and happiness." He's focused on ensuring that employees stay satisfied enough not to need to organize in the first place, but he's willing to cross that bridge if it comes.

Overall, Kim says, EL-VI can deal with new rules as long as they're applied evenly to all farms. Certainly, not all farms are as economically stable or well-managed as EL-VI, helmed by its team of unrelated partner-owners. Other farms in New York will struggle more to adapt to the new regulations. But isn't that kind of the point? If the only thing keeping a farm solvent is worker exploitation, we shouldn't want that farm to stick around. The same is true across the country, with issues from worker abuse to environmental degradation to food safety. The farms we want to populate our system will be willing and able to follow rules that protect the public interest. Our responsibility is to create and enforce those rules.

EDUCATING ABOUT REGENERATIVE? CENTER BIPOC FARMERS

Supporting and enriching Indigenous farmers, tenders, and teachers is critical for the future of our farm and food system. Although there has been a surge of interest in regenerative farming practices, with many public institutions offering educational programs on the subject, too often Indigenous voices are excluded. These programs often fail to acknowledge the Indigenous roots of regenerative ag and permaculture. This omission is painful and negligent, and it sets up farmers in these programs to misapply the principles, often in harmful ways.

"I want to see Indigenous people in some of these mainstream movements, whether it be regenerative, sustainable agriculture, or the permaculture movement," says A-dae Romero-Briones, the director of programs of Native Agriculture and Food Systems for the First Nations Development Institute, who has done some of this work herself. "We're starting to see more but it's not normal right now; it's a novelty when an Indigenous person is in these spaces." A-dae advocates for the inclusion of Indigenous stories in particular as part of this agricultural teaching because the stories help people understand the why behind the practices, rather than just the what and the how. Those stories hold the wisdom needed to implement practices appropriately in varying and ever-changing circumstances.

Further, I think it's essential for organizations operating in this space to acknowledge that education has its limitations as a solution to the farm system's problems. There are a plethora of existing opportunities in nearly every state and county in the US to learn farming and food production skills, often more or less for free. But these programs absolutely favor the already privileged, demonstrating that the problem in our farming system is not a lack of access to information or education but a lack of access to enough wealth and resources to make farming a viable livelihood.

I would wager that there are currently thousands, if not tens of thousands, of workers in the US who are highly skilled in agricultural production yet are not working in farming. With access to affordable land and other resources, and enough wealth to secure them, many of these folks could be farming right now. What new and beginning farmers really need are more creative and innovative pathways to accessing resources and building sustainable farm businesses that can retain them. Bigger, more diverse, and more professionalized teams can offer that stability, and often have a better chance of accessing the resources they need as well.

So, if your goal is to increase the number of new and beginning farmers in the US, consider skipping the quarterly seminars on tomato production. Instead, host an organizing session where those interested in food and farming businesses can meet, network, and learn from business leaders in other sectors about how to bring together a founding team, how to access financing for a small business, and how to think about capital investments. These entrepreneurial skills are much more inaccessible to those in the agricultural space, as are places where aspiring farmers can meet possible business partners.

DON'T LET A GOOD CRISIS PASS

When it comes to making radical changes in farming policy, crises—be they political, economic, or climatic—are usually the best moments to take big swings. Ricardo Salvador thinks there may be an opening in the next few years to have a fundamentally transformative discussion, for example, about the Farm Bill.

"The Farm Bill was designed to be reexamined every five years," he explains, "but it turns out that things are moving so quickly with climate change that five years may not be often enough." As the size and cost of ad hoc spending and emergency programs have ballooned in the last few years, the relevance of the Farm Bill continues to decline, basically because so much happens in the between years that the legislation is essentially being continuously rewritten. On top of that, the most recent farm aid programs have opened up the direct payment doors to crops that have never received them before. And, much like Pandora's box, once a new group receives a subsidy payment it is tough to claw it back.

There are two routes to policy change here. The first would involve a general recognition that the needs of the agricultural industry can't be foreseen for five years at a time, which could lead to proactive reform of how farm programs are framed and authorized. The second and more likely route seems to be that we will do nothing and continue to escalate direct farm payments year after year, regardless of Farm Bill language, and include more and more crops all the time. Eventually, the scope of farm spending is likely to become untenable to the American public. An ever-increasing amount of direct financial support to that tiny (and shrinking) group of Americans involved in agriculture will threaten the already tenuous political support that the Farm Bill, and other farm legislation, needs to pass.

The kind of farm policy crash this could cause, and related economic impact, could be avoided by planning ahead rather than waiting for the system to crumble under its own weight. What it takes is a clear vision and organization now.

FARMS CAN'T SAVE THE PLANET

In our increasingly climate-anxious world, the idea that we can farm our way to reversing global climate change is one of the most hopeful messages around. It's also a myth (Mitchell, 2020). Not least because, even if we could somehow undo hundreds of years of landscape and soil damage quickly enough to help stave off the worst effects of climate change, Earth's soil simply cannot absorb all the fossil carbon that has been released into the atmosphere by burning fossil fuel.

Despite its deep flaws, this idea is politically expedient. It has led to a lot of interest from farmers who are eager to get paid to invest in the long-term health of their own, privately owned land (in essence, being paid to do the rational thing). Politicians, business leaders, and even environmental groups have adopted this idea as a favored talking point; the concept that we don't have to farm less or reckon with sprawling, systemic issues, we just have to pay farmers to adopt a few climate-smart practices and achieve a win for all involved.

For the sake of our planet, for the sake of the people who have been excluded from the farming system for centuries, and for the sake of the next generation of American food producers, we have to abandon this bad idea.

It is no more possible to farm our way to a healthier planet than it is to shop our way to a more just food system. Paying farmers to plant a few cover crops is just as futile as a consumer trying to shop ethically at a big box store. Both activities miss the point by insisting that deep, system-wide problems can be affected by individual actions. It's worth noting that the difference between these two activities, however, is consumers are expected to pay more for their trouble whereas farmers, who are almost universally wealthier than the average American, expect to get paid.

An obsessive and myopic focus on environmental outcomes will inevitably miss many of the key drivers that brought American agriculture to where it is today. Pretending that farming, or sequestering carbon in soils, will save us wastes precious time on a nonsolution. It diverts public funds to paying already-wealthy farmers and landowners to do work already incentivized by the nature of private property. Focusing on this farce further entrenches the system in a way that disadvantages realistic alternatives which could actually achieve the kinds of outcomes we seek.

REMEMBER THAT FARMS ARE BUSINESSES

The exciting thing about most of the big team farms I found while researching this book is that many are successful. Few of them are raking in huge piles of money, yet they largely appear more stable than their small family farm counterparts who are often hanging on by a thread—a bad harvest away from bankruptcy or burnout.

It's fair to expect that big team farms grow and find stability at similar rates to small business in other sectors. They can be expected to aggressively pursue market opportunities, carefully track their financials, maintain strong relationships with their communities and customers, and attract smart, successful team members that help them stay ahead of the competition.

That doesn't mean big team farms never struggle. All businesses struggle, but they tend not to languish there. They're less likely to cling to tradition for tradition's sake and, in the cases where things truly go wrong, their professional failures don't sit exclusively on individual shoulders. Big team farms tend to work hard to be competitive organizations. And, in most cases, when they need outside capital or other resources, they want to find and secure it on their own terms. They usually don't need to be saved.

So, what's the role of policy making in this big team farm world? Clear the path. Ensure that policy isn't undercutting their efforts. Ensure that regulation is strengthening environmental protections so that taxpayers (including both big team farmers and their customers) aren't paying for the poor farming practices of other farmers. Ensure that their competitors aren't being propped up and kept on the land to degrade it, driving up land prices and making it harder for a new generation to find their way to agriculture. Ensure that the small family farm narrative is no longer held up as the pinnacle of American virtue at the expense of farmers, farmworkers, consumers, and the environment. If we want new things to come into being and grow, we've got to let old things die out.

We love small businesses because they are economic engines that create jobs and livelihoods as well as great products and services in our communities. Farms should not be an exception to this expectation. Public support for farm operations should be directly related to their ability to create good-paying, long-term, community-supporting jobs.

EMPOWER THE PEOPLE TO FEED THEMSELVES

The anthropological observations and demographic research in *Pressure Cooker: Why Home Cooking Won't Solve Our Problems and What We Can Do About It* by Sarah Bowen, Joslyn Brenton, and Sinikka Elliott, offer unequivocal evidence that low-income people have the same desires and preferences when it comes to eating and feeding their families as their wealthier neighbors. The desire for organic options, healthy, fresh, delicious, and easy-to-prepare foods were common among people at all income levels.

The evidence also suggests that cheap, unhealthy food is not a miracle cure for hunger. America is inundated with cheap, unhealthy food at this very moment, yet hunger and malnutrition persist at astronomical levels. This is largely because hunger is not a crisis of agriculture as much as it is a political condition.

Hunger is an intersectional issue that results not from superficial caloric scarcity but from the much bigger, existential issues related to wealth inequality. Debates about food access, regulation, and labor, animal, and environmental protections often circle back to the idea that food must remain cheap at all costs so that the poorest Americans can afford it. That, in its own way, is a form of bottom-line thinking in the political economy, because cheap food isn't the only or best way to ensure that people are fed. Paying workers a living wage, especially workers within the food system, allows more people to afford more food and gives them more choice when they go to the store. Seven of the ten worst-paid jobs in America are in the food system (Tepper, 2013). We should start there if we want to address food access.

In short, the cheap food stipulation is a distraction from the real issues we should be discussing—it uses the poor as a shield behind which bad actors can hide public funds and avoid rules and regulations. In my conversation with Andrew deCoriolis of Farm Future, he pointed out an example of this diversion tactic in the debate around a recent proposition in California to regulate the use of battery cage gestation crates for pigs.

"The argument against [this regulation] that the industry put forward," Andrew says, "was that the cost of animal products will go up, that pork would get more expensive, and that's an equity problem. So some food access advocates, people who run food banks, for example, came out against the proposition, saying if we regulate battery cages poor people will go hungry. But poor people go hungry anyway. That's an economic decision we made as a country; it has essentially nothing to do with production practices."

So rather than obsessing with lowering costs in agriculture to keep prices low, we should focus on investing in our society's most vulnerable people. Rather than focusing on cheap food, we could focus on ensuring that more of the money amassed by high-net-worth individuals, companies, and other organizations makes its way to workers by way of an increased minimum wage or even a universal basic income that ensures access to food. When we demand that food be cheap, we assume that poverty is a given. Cheap food isn't the only way to prevent hunger. Enriching workers is much more effective.

Remember, food is not just calories. Food is sacred. Food, and the interdependence that's required to feed us all, is one of the glues that bind us together as a society. When policy fails to recognize the sacredness of food, it erodes its own usefulness and creates crises that threaten its own legitimacy.

CHAPTER 9

The Rest of Us

———

If you are anything like me, you may have gotten to the end of this book and realized that you might not be up to starting or joining a farm, big or small. I think that's okay. First, that realization acknowledges that, despite all of the ways our agrarian myths convince us otherwise, farming just isn't accessible to all. It's not an enterprise to take up lightly, and humans aren't born with the knowledge required to grow food. Farming is a specialized skill, usually acquired over the course of a lifetime.

But deciding against farming as a profession doesn't mean we have no role to play in our food and farming system. We have many varied and significant roles, and they aren't the well-worn maxims of "shop at the farmers market," "buy organic," or "ask a farmer." The things we can do that would really make an impact on our food and farm system require more than that: a deeper interrogation of our preconceived notions around the way we see food, land, and, most importantly, one another.

But that's not exactly concrete. If you're looking for more specific advice, read on.

STOP TRYING TO SAVE FARMS

Before you pitch into the next farm GoFundMe, or attend the next farm benefit concert, ask yourself an important question: Why does this farm need to be saved? Are these businesses serving a need in our communities and doing the work we expect a good farm to do? Or is this a case of a private individual or family seeking support to hold on to both wealth and the identity that property ownership grants them?

On a deeper level, if we really do want to help farms, our commitments likely have to go beyond writing checks. Handing over money to farmers has been our entire strategy of improving the agricultural system for the last four hundred years, and it has been an arduous failure. So, if you know of a community-serving, employee-enriching, environmentally conscious farm that, for whatever reason, falls on hard times and reaches out to its community for assistance—cash can help in the short-term but long-term stability likely requires a more detailed examination of the organization's unique problems. Make sure someone is asking why the farm ended up in crisis in the first place.

The answer to this question might be simply that the deck of capitalism is stacked against them, and the tangible or intangible value they add to the community is greater than the financial aid they seek. Even when this is the case, interrogate whether a one-time cash infusion is really the answer. Will this farm need this kind of support regularly to continue? If that's so, maybe the profit model being pursued isn't working and needs to be changed considerably, or maybe there are other creative interventions to pursue. If the community is investing significant funds, make sure that the community has a seat at the table when making decisions about how the farm operates in the future.

DEFY THE GATEKEEPERS

If you care about the food system—and, gosh, you've made it an awful long way through this book if you don't—you've probably, at some point or another, been shut down in a conversation about the food system in one of the following ways:

- "Seems like you're confused! You should go straight to the source and ask a farmer."
- "You didn't grow up on a farm; you could never really understand."
- "I've been farming all my life. I think what I have to say matters more than your opinion."
- "I hear your concerns but you just don't get it. Things are different when it comes to agriculture. Your experience has no bearing here."
- "If you and other consumers just understood where your food comes from, you'd be grateful for everything farmers do for this country."

These are just a few of the ways I've heard entrenched players gaslight, gate-keep, badger, and harass thoughtful people out of conversations about farming and its role in the food system. In fact, many people get badgered, harassed, and "little lady"-ed right out the industry altogether.

This exclusion is by design. The insularity of the current agricultural sector is essential to its continued existence because only allowing certain voices to be heard allows realities of the system to go unrecognized and unquestioned by consumers and lawmakers alike.

For example, research shows that most consumers don't think the US food system is headed in the right direction: due to outstanding concerns about everything from the use of pesticides and chemical fertilizers to confined animal agriculture (U.S. Farmers and Ranchers Alliance, 2011). This is not news to the industry. Making sure these less-savory parts of farming stay out of sight of consumers has been a priority for decades. As the farm sector has consolidated and farmers have replaced physical labor with technology, the declining number of people involved in farming has facilitated this erosion of public oversight. In that way, those removed from the farm are better able to cling to their ideas of the sacred American farmer, which has been extremely beneficial for agriculture's public image. And it's worked—despite all the dislike of modern practices, agriculture is still the most trusted industry in the US, according to consumers (Graber, 2021).

The gap in the public imagination between the fantasy and the reality of farms has only expanded over time. Fighting to maintain the opacity and mystique around farming is critical if the industry hopes to stay up on the pedestal where many have placed it. The agriculture industry is like a high wall of fog around a house of cards, where protectors of the status quo mill around, pointing you away from the truth when you get too near, often by questioning your right to ask questions or participate in the conversation at all.

So if you decide to wade into public discussions about farming and the food system with anything besides "agvocacy" in mind, this gatekeeping will happen to you. My best advice? Call out the gatekeepers.

If you are a US taxpayer, the agriculture sector has benefited from your contribution to the billions of dollars in subsidies they've received over your lifetime. As an investor in the farm and food system, you've earned the right to have a say. As a consumer, you have the right to ask questions, have opinions, and challenge authority in sectors where you participate. Your lack of experience in the technical aspects of farming in no way makes you unable to comment or question a farm's practices, just as you don't need to be a civil engineer to ask whether we should build a dam that will flood a town. Common sense is its own expertise.

You are smart. You are informed. You know things and have had experiences that some farmers could never imagine, and that diversity of insight and opinion should make the system stronger, not weaker. There is space for all and elevating more collaborators does not diminish the existing ones.

Don't let the gatekeepers shut you out. All voices are needed here.

STOP SAYING FARMERS MUST FEED THE WORLD

I was in ninth grade the first time I heard that, in 2050, there will be nine billion people on the planet. Since then, I've encountered endless speeches, articles, and tweets about how farmers, particularly in the US, are now feeding, or must in the future, feed the world. We hear it from all sides, from those defending genetically modified crops to those advocating for the end of animal agriculture to those looking to turn farming into a tool to counter climate change.

Many of the world's wealthy are taking an interest in this ambitious task as well, with research and demonstration farms becoming the pet projects of many a billionaire or major company (Amelinckx, 2015). Their aim seems to be to show that with the right intention and "a little start-up capital," farms can feed the world without destroying it (Soper, 2019).

But the idea that farmers feed the world is a total crock. The question, "How do we farm to feed the world?" doesn't even make sense. Farming and feeding people are, in our globalized world, almost completely disconnected.

In fact, I'd argue that, in the American context, we do not farm to feed the world at all. We "feed the world" because we want to keep farming and making money doing it. We've tapped out US markets for the crops that farmers like to grow best—high-yield, low-labor crops like commodity corn, soybeans, cotton, and confined livestock—so farmers need global markets to absorb the excess product they don't want to stop producing.

So how do we rethink the relationship between farming and global hunger?

First, we must acknowledge that it is nonsensical to put the mission of averting starvation on the shoulders of armers, in the US or anywhere else. Hunger is a complex issue with many social and political dimensions. The quantity of food produced is rarely the fundamental problem. We also must stop letting farmers and other people in agriculture justify bad behavior (like harming workers and ecosystems, violating regulations, and so on) by claiming they're trying to "feed the world."

Further, we have to recognize that food sovereignty and food security are in themselves sacred goals for people across the globe. It's reasonable that people outside of the US don't want to depend on the overproduction of US farmers to have enough to eat. The world wants to feed itself.

Second, we must acknowledge that as long as we continue to associate farming with feeding the world, we perpetuate extractive tendencies. After all, if farms have to "feed the world" then farms *must* maximize output. If they don't grow the highest possible quantity of crops, people will starve. But that's fundamentally not true. Again, we already grow enough calories to feed the world more than once over. We don't need to suck every possible calorie out of our soils, water, forests, or animals. If you believe the future of agriculture lies in optimizing farms by tailoring them to their conditions, local markets, and people, and not in bleeding the landscape dry, it doesn't make sense to connect farming and feeding the world. That idea is harmful because it celebrates maximum output and demonizes farms that prioritize their long-term sustainability over high yields. It gives cover to bad actors and saddles the rest with the guilt of not doing enough to end global hunger.

Finally, though farms are not the be-all and end-all of the food system or of improving global food access, healthy parts do contribute to healthy wholes. If we can make farms stable and sustainable, they would contribute to a system that could feed the world in a just and inclusive way. But we'll definitely need collaboration with a lot of other moving parts: including effective distribution, peace, political stability, regulated markets, sturdy infrastructure, reduced wealth inequality, and more.

So stop saying that farmers need to feed the world. Stop writing it. Stop thinking it. Don't let people around you use the catchy cliché, for inspiration or excuse. Don't take it at face value when you read it or hear it and push back on it when you can. We have to dig deeper by pressing ourselves and others to learn about and understand the complexity of our food systems and all the factors that affect them.

STOP TRYING TO VOTE WITH YOUR FORK

As an agriculture reporter I hear a lot of speeches, manifestos, and diatribes about why people eat organic, vegetarian, or vegan, when they started avoiding gluten or dairy, or how they got turned on to pickling or kombucha. A common revelation in all these stories is people saying they realized the need to "vote with their fork." In other words, somewhere on their food journey, they figured out that they, personally, could and must act as the omnipotent change agent. They are to secure safety, justice, and environmental integrity in the American food system. They took pride in fulfilling this solemn obligation on every trip to the organic grocery store or their favorite local farm-to-table restaurant.

This idea has permeated our cultural landscape for decades, promoted by food and farm celebrities and advocates. I think Michael Pollan captured the concept of "eating for change" best in a 2006 *New York Times* article when he wrote: "You can simply stop participating in a system that abuses animals or poisons the water or squanders jet fuel flying asparagus around the world. You can vote with your fork, in other words, and you can do it three times a day."

What he's saying here is that registering your discontent with how a product is made, distributed, or sold is as simple as just not buying it. Eventually the wrong will be righted, and you can go on your merry way, content that you've done all the heavy lifting required to spark a revolution. Essentially, if we just try hard enough, we can consume our way to a better world.

It's an idea that feels breathtakingly simple, fundamentally transformative, utterly attainable, and it's total nonsense.

On the individual level, we can tell ourselves that vegetarianism or veganism excuses us from any guilt over animal abuse, or that we are shrinking our carbon footprint by only buying local. But the idea of voting with our forks doesn't limit the scope of its effect to the personal. It promises systemic change that will ripple through every echelon of society. But making these tweaks in our consumer choices is deeply unlikely to make a difference to the larger system.

To begin with, most people can't or won't "shop ethically." The poorest 40 percent of Americans already spend between 20–35 percent of their income on food (USDA ERS, 2021). As food prices climbed in late 2021 and early 2022, many more American households have struggled to eat at all (Schwartz, 2021), much less "eat for change." Our food insecure neighbors cannot "simply stop participating" in food systems they disagree with without putting their lives, and the lives of their families, at risk.

On top of that, American food shopping habits are still overwhelmingly driven by price (Jayasinghe, 2016). Even for people for whom paying more is financially viable, there is a dearth of knowledge or incentive that would lead them to decide to buy $2 onions when they're sitting next to $0.99 onions that look almost the same. Votes only work if you can get a majority, and on the current trajectory there may well never be a majority voting for a "better" food system.

Furthermore, it's essentially impossible to know enough about what you buy, even among the well-informed. Short of sourcing all your food from a single local farm or group of farms and always cooking at home, you'll likely never be able to cast a clear and uncomplicated "yea" vote. And for most Americans, shopping that way would mean cutting sugar, coffee, tropical fruits like bananas, oranges, avocados, and many other staple products out of their diet. Even the most knowledgeable and well-intentioned middle- and upper-class consumers would likely not opt for this sacrifice.

Instead, most people who care about food, health, and agriculture do a partial vote. We look out for keywords in the grocery store: "natural," "organic," "grass-fed," "local," "fair trade," and other indicators that we are making the "right" choice, like an unfamiliar brand with a suitably hipster or wholesome label. We say no to the brands we were raised on and opt instead for new ones that make promises like "small batch," "ethically-sourced," and "sustainable." And we feel good about a basket full of edgy and ethical alt food, and happily fork over the extra cash to get it.

But there's an entire branding trend that's taking advantage of your instinct to do this. Many of these "indie" food products are owned by the same multinationals whose products our parents fed us growing up (Wells, 2016). The problem is, most of us don't have hours and hours to spend researching companies, the definitions of marketing terms, the standards for FDA labels, and the intricacies of various production practices. We try our best with the knowledge we have, and companies know that. A change in the font on the label is all it takes to reel us right back into the arms of the same organizations that got our food system here in the first place.

Why do they do it? Because the food system is an interconnected web of companies, from farmers to processors, to wholesalers, retailers, and restaurants, that get food from seed to fork. For these companies, change is expensive, and the dominant players won't be easily dislodged. They designed the food system for maximum profit and doing so has provisioned them with the resources to put up a serious fight.

The "vote with your fork" line tells us we don't have to dislodge these players because it's in their best interest to respond to what consumers want. But that has, overwhelmingly, not been the case. The cheapest way to "adapt to consumer demands" has always been to identify changing desires and rebrand your existing products to align. The murky legal definitions in the food world for terms like "ethically-sourced" and "sustainable" make these changes relatively easy. When minor tweaks are common—like the "natural" Jif peanut butter which substituted an artificially hydrogenated oil for a naturally hydrogenated one, or McDonald's switching from white bags to "natural" brown—it's clear that the priority is too often cosmetic, not systemic, change (Cain, 2010).

If somehow a rebrand doesn't work for a product, another good option is to convince consumers that they've been misled about their newfound preference for a better product. A company might point out what makes them different from a competitor even if it's inconsequential—see the Super Bowl beer ad that bragged about "no corn syrup," even though the beer in question contained rice syrup, which is nearly the same thing (Smith, 2019). They might cloud the water so consumers won't possibly know what to believe and increase the likelihood they'll revert to brands and products they've trusted in the past. They might use the same images, words, and emotions that led to the shift in demand and paint their product as part of the shift. Alongside a company's public insistence that consumer demands have been heard, a token charitable contribution always helps.

It's also common for a company to outright own both their own traditional product and its new "ethical" competitors. Are customers switching from cow's milk to organic almond milk? Why not just own a dairy brand and a nut beverage brand? Companies can claim they're simultaneously responding to consumer demand for "ethical" milk while looking out for consumers who need a more affordable product. Do they make it clear to nut beverage customers that the premium they pay ungirds traditional dairy products as well? Of course not.

With their colossal organizations, overcompensated executives, and shareholders fueled by sheer greed, it's likely that supporting sustainable practices, paying workers a fair wage, and investing in healthy products are viewed as unnecessary expenses to the legacy players in the food industry. Now, and for the foreseeable future, it seems that actually making these changes will continue to be a last resort.

Perhaps the most significant impact of two decades of "voting with our forks" is that it's made food companies experts at getting people to empty their wallets for products that are, at best, marginal ethical improvements. The alternative food movement has been a boon for the marketing industry and food companies who thought they'd never get people to spend more for the same amount of food. Not to mention that research on how packaging, labels, and even placement in stores drives food purchases illustrates that companies have an incredible amount of control over "what consumers want" anyway, and it's almost always the products that earn companies the most profit.

What I try to communicate to people when they're through telling me about how and why they eat and don't eat the things they eat and don't eat is that, it's great that they're thinking about food and staying engaged. But it's also not our individual responsibilities to pay our way to a better food system, and it probably isn't possible anyway. Consumers didn't make the food system. And I hope everyone has many probing questions for anyone who tells you it's your job to fix it. Because the idea that throwing a few extra dollars into our food budget makes us change agents is an awfully easy way to fix something that's been centuries in the making, and awfully profitable for the players who got us here. In that way, we're paying companies to make us feel good, not to actually do good. Offering these kinds of easy, do-it-yourself, feel-good solutions is a great way to sell books and newspapers but not a great way to make meaningful change.

Ultimately, reassigning the burden of transformation to consumers, or any other group, is a painless way for companies to wash their hands of guilt. "We're just giving people what they want," is a great excuse because the subtext is that they don't have a choice—the poor, global food conglomerate batted about by the winds of idle consumer whims. But food companies do have a choice. They could cut their marketing budgets and pay for more ethical farm practices. They could price imports to accurately reflect the cost of cleaning up the carbon emissions from air shipping. They could stop using their exorbitant profits to fuel lobbying that secures favorable regulations, which allow them to prioritize profits over the public good. They could get smaller, allow for more competition in the food space, stop buying up every upstart food company that in any way threatens their existing product lines, and truly subject themselves to a free, competitive market that rewards innovation. They could make those choices, but they don't. Buying into the "consumers are responsible" narrative just reinforces the fictional helplessness of billion-dollar corporations, and somehow gets you to pay them more for the privilege of their manipulation.

The very idea of voting with your fork is really the greatest marketing scheme of all.

THINK DEEPER AND EAT WELL

If you really care about a better food system, vote with your vote. Elect leaders who will change the incentives around key issues like marketing, food labeling, farming, labor practices, environmental protection, and food and consumer safety. And once they're elected, keep them honest.

Then, consider saving the money you would spend buying high-priced, "ethical" versions of your staples and donating it to a mutual aid network or other group that feeds your community instead. Some CSAs even allow members to donate a membership to a person or family in need. Helping the food insecure have access to more and better-quality food is a better use of your money than padding the profits of the multinational that bought your favorite indie food brand. Plus, if you can send more money to a local food provider, you can feel good about knowing that you're keeping more money in your community.

Finally, eat and don't panic. Get fast food sometimes. Cook a few meals at home. Eat pizza rolls. Get a salad from that corner spot. Snack your way through the farmers market. Try whatever pumpkin-spice-flavored novelty is selling next to the register. Swipe eight chocolates from a coworker's desk. Experiment with steel-cut oats, and toss them if you don't like how it turns out. Learn all the different ways to make eggs. Get drunk and eat food truck tacos. Recognize that fixing a global system is a difficult problem that can only be solved with a lot of effort by a lot of people, over a long time. One person can't solve it, it's not your job to do alone, and eating the food that makes you happy is not you failing to do your part. You're thinking, you're trying, and you're doing great. Now let's keep going.

FIND YOUR HOME TEAM

So if conscious consumerism isn't the answer, what is?

Well, first of all, if you're really passionate about the food and farm system, and you have relevant skills, think about working at a big team farm.

If you love your job, or work in some other field, but you're still passionate about the food system, you need to find your home team, by which I mean your local big team farms. This work might start at a farmers market but it might start elsewhere too, wherever you eat. But it goes deeper than picking up a couple in-season tomatoes for $8 a pound. First, talk to the vendors. Get to know them. Ask them if the market is profitable for them. Ask them if they're really charging enough for their products. Find your own data points, ones with faces, stories, and passions. Abandon the fruitless obligation to read that long *New Yorker* feature about superfoods or horrible labor abuses, and instead spend some time making the tomato guy *your* tomato guy.

While you're asking questions and listening to the answers, share about yourself as well. Be candid. Tell Tomato Guy that their produce is too expensive or that the market is at a bad time for you. Tell them that sometimes you make it to the market, but more often than not you have to run to the local grocery store to get last-minute items. Ask about and offer suggestions for making things more convenient and cost-efficient for you. Have them over for dinner and introduce them to your neighbors. Tell them about your family and learn about theirs, about their goals and dreams, and why they do what they do.

You may have caught on here but what I'm recommending is that you build a personal relationship with farmers and other people passionate about food and farming in your community. Not a transactional one where, when you remember, you go to the market and pay a premium to take home warm fuzzies and Instagram posts than food. I mean a real, complex relationship. The kind where you send each other holiday cards, where you're on the e-mail list for a new baby announcement, and where you can text each other memes when the occasion arises.

This is the work of supporting big team farms. There's no easy, simple consumer rule of thumb to follow, no cute slogans. You just have to really, deeply care about people.

It's definitely not easy work. But if this book has been about one thing, it's that no part of farming is easy. Human work is hard work. But that makes doing it so much more worthwhile. When you are truly privy to the ins and outs of your food community, you'll be able to engage reciprocally, rather than transactionally, with the people who grow your food. What will that look like exactly? I can't say. It'll be unique in every case. You'll know you're doing it right when, from time to time, it hurts.

TAKE ALTERNATIVES SERIOUSLY

I've shared the facts, ideas, and advice captured in this book countless times, both publicly and privately. And I've been dismissed on many occasions, often waved off with a "That's just not practical," or, "Maybe that would have worked in the past, but not anymore." I've heard that the globalized food system, the size of the world population, and the dire threat of climate change, among many others, are all reasons why collectivism, communalism, collaboration, and deep human connections simply cannot be the way forward for the American food and farm system.

My best response to all these dismissals is: Who says? The historical evidence suggests that collectivism, commons, and deep human connections have been very effective farm strategies in the past (Mock, 2021). In fact, we may well have more evidence that food and farming systems based on interdependence are more successful and resilient than any other.

Rarely are these dismissals about the facts. Usually, when we instinctively diminish ideas that don't conform to the logic of capitalism, we're mostly admitting our own ignorance. The reality is we in the dominant American culture don't often get exposed to ideas or stories that clash with capitalist principles, and when we do it's usually about how experiments with alternatives to capitalism have failed. But that doesn't mean that alternatives have never existed or worked. On the contrary, many exist and work today; we either just don't recognize them for what they are, or their stories are marginalized or erased because they don't conform to our expectations.

Moving past these knee-jerk reactions of thinking that alternatives are "impractical" or "old-fashioned" requires deep interrogation of our instinct to dismiss things that are different in this way. If we have a limited knowledge about alternatives to capitalist structures, as the vast majority of Americans do, then why do we feel so confident in knowing whether or not they could work?

All this to say, whether you're getting shut down for sharing an unconventional solution or find yourself doing the shutting down, remember that in our own lives and communities, each and every one of us participates in setting the table. The ideas that get a seat are the ones we allow to sit down. Every idea that we dismiss out of hand, whenever or wherever we dismiss it, is a possible future destroyed. In that way, we decide every day what is possible by what we choose to believe in, to share, to argue for, and to honor. There is not a divine, predetermined list out there of what is good and bad, possible and impossible. There is a universe of ideas and futures, and the ones that receive our time, care, and attention are the ones that grow.

FORGET THE AGRARIAN FANTASY...

Today we pay for our "small family farm" fantasy, and the cost is too high. Bad farmers, shielded by our romantic notions and the decisions we make because of them, pollute our air and water, wash away topsoil, denude forests, cause algal blooms, and subject plants and animals to horrible conditions that compromise their evolution and our own. We pay when beaches close and when species go extinct. Bad farmers abuse workers, endanger consumers, and damage the public trust. We can't afford bad farmers anymore. We need farmers who know that the essential function of their farm is to grow good food and good jobs, and to do so without ruining our landscapes.

...BUT UNDERSTAND WHY IT RESONATED IN THE FIRST PLACE

You may have gotten all the way here, to the very end of this book, and still nurse a seed of doubt about these conclusions. I know, because I do too.

When I question the agrarian fantasy of the small family farm that lives inside me, I understand why farmers, and the rest of us, fight so hard to preserve the illusion and protect the people who embody it.

It's because land is not just a thing. Land is not just an economic idea, or a means to an end. Geography is powerful; it lives inside us. We know this intuitively, even subconsciously, and through our empathy we can understand why a farmer, or a farm family, would fight to the death to maintain that connection.

But the thing is, that very feeling is evidence that it's not only farmers who feel a deep connection to land and place. We all crave that same sense of home and belonging, of safety and security. Sure, we have apartments, houses, lawns, and gardens, and we treasure them, but it's just not the same. It doesn't have the same pull as the idea of homeland—a place big enough to feed a community, to bury our dead and keep them close, and to grow, expand, and explore. We all crave that physical freedom: to be outside, to work with our hands, to feel the healing and soothing effects of being around soil, flowing water, and plants.

We all crave the opportunity to live and work in a place where we have continuity. Most of us, however, will never have the privilege. We have been forced, by violence or economics, to move to cities and suburbs, separated from the land artificially. I count myself in the cohort of people who nurse a love for the place where they were born, yet who are unable to see a viable path to return. The economic, cultural, and social barriers are just too high. And so I'll stay where I am, as so many have before me, in an impersonal and forever-temporary apartment, wandering city streets in search of evidence that the land around me is living and not dead. I miss my family. I feel untethered. Nobody wants to feel this way.

And yet we look at landowners—those who get the opportunity to live this life so many of us fantasize about—and rather than asking these privileged few what they can do to help others share in the peace and joy of settlement, we ask what we, the dispossessed, can do to help them maintain their privilege. We ask what we can do to ensure their family farm stays exclusive to their kin and that they are not bothered by the longing of lowly city-slickers like us.

When we defend a farmer's desire to own a few hundred or thousand acres of farmland because of its personal significance, how many others' attachments do we deny?

A few thousand acres, throughout much of the US, could provide many, many people a place on the land, and the satisfaction of that bone-deep desire for home that we all have. A few thousand acres, carefully managed, could feed and care for them all. It could be a homeland for many. And if so many "save the farm" campaigns, concerts, and rallies have been inspired to help just a few people to hang on to their homeland, imagine how enormous our response could be to help hundreds of thousands of people return to the lands that they or their ancestors called home or to find new places to which they can become naturalized.

Genetic ancestry does not dictate your ability to become native to a place. European and Euro-American people in North America, as a group, have largely not yet learned how to be good guests, good neighbors, and to do our part to contribute what gifts we have while curtailing our destructive tendencies as part of the landscape. We have mostly failed to understand how to find fulfillment without exploiting our home and each other. In general, we have not yet learned how to participate in our environment and have, instead, too often devoted our energy to propping up the artifice that we are above or outside it somehow. But it is not too late to start learning and to make amends, *real* amends, for the damage already done.

Carl Sagan famously said that "we are made of star-stuff." This is true and amazing, and—despite all Sagan's pioneering work in decentering humankind, Earth, and even the Milky Way in the universe—this statement makes us feel important, extraordinary, and rare. But it's worth remembering that everything around us—animals, plants, soil, water, rocks—is also made of star-stuff. Furthermore, we humans have about 80 percent of our genetic material in common with cattle and 60 percent in common with bananas. Every person on Earth is 99.9 percent alike to the next. In other words, we are indiscernible from our world. Our collective sacredness is intertwined. The selfish thing to do then, to protect and preserve ourselves, requires that we protect and preserve food, land, the world, and one another.

Our scientific knowledge alone demands that we have a fundamental reckoning with the way we produce food, not least because we are rapidly farming ourselves and our fellow Earthlings into a largely uninhabitable planet. We know that our settler-extraction style of farming is the culprit behind many of our problems. We can no longer pretend that there's a world of independent, small family farmers out there that elevate the public interest over their desire to perpetuate intergenerational wealth. We have four hundred years of evidence to the contrary.

It's time for our love affair with the ephemeral agrarian fantasy to come to an end. It's time to evict the idea from our hearts and minds and instead elevate other stories and strategies, like those collective and communal methods invented, refined, and sustained by farmers of color across time. These blueprints not only offer marginalized farmers the opportunity to reclaim a homeland, to reconnect with work, to feed their communities, and care for the earth, but they might just offer the rest of us the opportunity to do the same.

Acknowledgments

This book, like its predecessor, is the product of a big team of people, including many who challenged me deeply about my conclusions and read early versions to offer thoughtful and provocative feedback. Those include my excellent editors: Julia Tanaka and Joanna Hatzikazakis, in addition to Connie Bowen, Reana Kovalcik, Mackenzie Gross, Hopey Fink, Mariko Thorbecke, Alison Grantham, and Errol Schweizer. And a special thanks to Bryan Dombrowski, who not only read what I wrote but also stayed by my side as I experienced some of the most exciting, transformative, and heartbreaking experiences of my life.

Once again, I want to acknowledge the many, many people who financially backed the publication of this book. It wouldn't exist if not for you, and there are no words to fully express my gratitude.

Appendix

___

INTERLUDE

Berke, Jeremy. "How Eating Meat Creates a 'Dead Zone' the Size of New Jersey in the Gulf of Mexico Every Year." *Business Insider*, April 7, 2018. https://www.businessinsider.com/eating-meat-affects-environment-dead-zone-2018-4.

Duff, Meaghan Noelle, *"This Famous Island in the Virginia Sea": The Influence of the Irish Tudor and Stuart Plantation Experiences in the Evolution of American Colonial Theory and Practice.* Williamsburg: College of William & Mary, 1992. https://dx.doi.org/doi:10.21220/s2-kvrp-3b47.

Merchant, James, and David Osterberg. *The Explosion of CAFOs in Iowa and Its Impact on Water Quality and Public Health.* Iowa City: The Iowa Policy Project, 2018. https://www.iowapolicyproject.org/2018docs/180125-CAFO.pdf.

Sauer, Amanda, and Suzie Greenhalgh. *Awakening the Dead Zone: An Investment for Agriculture, Water Quality, and Climate*

Change. Washington, DC: World Resource Institute, 2003.
https://files.wri.org/d8/s3fs-public/pdf/awaken_dead_zone.pdf.

US EPA (United States Environmental Protection Agency). *The
Effects: Dead Zones and Toxic Algal Blooms*. Accessed January
8, 2022. https://www.epa.gov/nutrientpollution/effects-dead-
zones-and-harmful-algal-blooms

CHAPTER 1 | WHOSE FARM?

Dolan, Kevin, Vivian Hunt, Sara Prince, and Sandra Sancier-
Sultan. "Diversity Still Matters." *McKinsey Quarterly*, May 19,
2020. https://www.mckinsey.com/featured-insights/diversity-
and-inclusion/diversity-still-matters.

Merriam-Webster. *The Lost Meanings of 'Farm' and 'Farmer.'*
Accessed January 8, 2022. https://www.merriam-webster.com/
words-at-play/the-origin-of-farm.

Rosenberg, Gabriel. "I Don't Hate Farmers." *The Strong Paw of
Reason* (email newsletter). Jan. 18, 2021. https://bearistotle.
substack.com/p/i-dont-hate-farmers.

Sullivan, Paul. "For Owners Looking to Sell, an Option That
Keeps Their Company Intact." *The New York Times*, Oct. 23,
2020. https://www.nytimes.com/2020/10/23/your-money/sale-
company-employees-esop.html.

CHAPTER 2 | GROW A PEOPLE-SYSTEM

Douglas, Leah. "Coronavirus Infections at U.S. Meat Plants
Far Higher than Previous Estimates -House Subcommit-

tee." *Reuters*, Oct. 27, 2021. https://www.reuters.com/world/us/coronavirus-infections-us-meat-plants-far-higher-than-previous-estimates-house-2021-10-27/.

Hamel, Gary. "Inside the World's Most Creatively Managed Company." *Harvard Business Review*, Dec. 2011. https://www.personalstrengths.ro/docs/2016/Harvard-Article.pdf.

Laloux, Frederic, and Ken Wilber. *Reinventing Organizations: A Guide to Creating Organizations Inspired by the Next Stage in Human Consciousness*. Brussels: Nelson Parker, 2014.

Rosenblatt, Lauren. "A Labor Shortage in Farming? That's Nothing New, Area Farmers Say, But It's Getting Worse." *Pittsburg Post-Gazette*, June 20, 2021. https://www.post-gazette.com/business/career-workplace/2021/06/20/Farming-labor-shortage-Western-Pennsylvania-minimum-wage-increase-H-2A-foreign-workers-visa/stories/202106200058.

Todd, Sarah. "There's No Such Thing as a Low Skilled Worker." *Quartz*, Aug. 13, 2021. https://www.yahoo.com/now/no-thing-low-skilled-worker-100137953.html.

Weinzweig, Ari. *A Lapsed Anarchist's Approach to Managing Ourselves*. Ann Arbor: Zingerman's Press, 2013.

CHAPTER 3 | FARMS ARE FOOD BUSINESSES

Gerber, Michael E. *The E Myth Revisited: Why Most Small Businesses Don't Work and What to Do about It*. New York: HarperCollins, 1995.

Holt Giménez, Eric. "We Already Grow Enough Food for 10 Billion People — And Still Can't End Hunger." *Huff Post*, December 18, 2014. https://www.huffpost.com/entry/world-hunger_b_1463429.

Quinn, Bob, and Liz Carlisle. *Grain by Grain: A Quest to Revive Ancient Wheat, Rural Jobs, and Healthy Food*. Washington, DC: Island Press, 2019.

Thilmany, Dawn, Becca Jablonski, Debra Tropp, Blake Angelo, and Sarah Low. *Mitigating Immediate Harmful Impacts of COVID-19 on Farms and Ranches Selling through Local and Regional Food Markets*. Washington, DC: National Sustainable Agriculture Coalition, 2020. https://localfoodeconomics.com/wp-content/uploads/2020/03/2020_03_21_EconomicImpactLocal Food-NSAC-SEH.pdf.

USDA ERS (United States Department of Agriculture Economic Research Service). *Food Prices and Spending*. Last updated December 27, 2021a. https://www.ers.usda.gov/data-products/ag-and-food-statistics-charting-the-essentials/food-prices-and-spending/.

USDA ERS (United States Department of Agriculture Economic Research Service). *Retailing and Wholesaling: Retail Trends*. Last updated Dec. 22, 2021b. https://www.ers.usda.gov/topics/food-markets-prices/retailing-wholesaling/retail-trends/.

CHAPTER 5 | IN THE BEGINNING OF A FARM BUSINESS

Pritchard, Forrest, and Ellen Polishuk. *Start Your Farm: The Authoritative Guide to Becoming a Sustainable 21st-Century Farmer.* New York: The Experiment, LLC, 2018.

CHAPTER 6 | IN THE THICK OF A FARM BUSINESS

Weinzweig, Ari. *A Lapsed Anarchist's Approach to Building a Great Business.* Ann Arbor: Zingerman's Press, 2010.

CHAPTER 7 | INVESTING IN BIG TEAM FARMS

Hager, Thomas. *The Alchemy of Air: A Jewish Genius, a Doomed Tycoon, and the Scientific Discovery That Fed the World but Fueled the Rise of Hitler.* New York: Harmony Books, 2008.

John Deere. "Farm Forward | John Deere Innovation and Technology." February 20, 2019. Video, 3:54. https://www.youtube.com/watch?v=nKAz-g7MAxs.

Mak, Adrien. "What Percentage of Small Businesses Fail?" *Advisor Smith*, May 4, 2021. https://advisorsmith.com/data/small-business-failure-rate/.

U.S. Farm Report. "John Phipps' Ugly Truth about Succession Planning: Unearned Wealth Brings Out the Worst in Everybody." *AgWeb*, January 31, 2022. https://www.agweb.com/news/business/succession-planning/john-phipps-ugly-truth-about-succession-planning-unearned-wealth#:~:text=My%20observation%20this%20issue%20has,even%20olives%20after%20your%20death.

CHAPTER 8 | POLICY FOR THE BI TEAM FUTURE

Daniel, Pete. *Dispossession: Discrimination against African American Farmers in the Age of Civil Rights.* Chapel Hill: The University of North Carolina Press, 2013.

Glauber, Joseph W., Daniel A. Sumner, and Parke E. Wilde. *Poverty, Hunger, and US Agricultural Policy: Do Farm Programs Affect the Nutrition of Poor Americans?* Washington, DC: American Enterprise Institute, 2017. https://www.aei.org/research-products/report/poverty-hunger-and-us-agricultural-policy-do-farm-programs-affect-the-nutrition-of-poor-americans.

Mitchell, Charlie. "Farmers Can't Save the Planet." *The New Republic*, August 7, 2020. https://newrepublic.com/article/158833/agribusiness-farms-microsoft-mcdonalds-carbon-climate-change.

Tepper, Rachel. "Lowest Paying Jobs in America: 7 Out of 10 Are in the Food Industry." *HuffPost*, April 2, 2013. https://www.huffpost.com/entry/lowest-paying-jobs-food-industry_n_2999799.

USDA ERS (United States Department of Agriculture Economic Research Service). *Farm Bill Spending.* Last updated October 19, 2021. https://www.ers.usda.gov/topics/farm-economy/farm-commodity-policy/farm-bill-spending.

Zulauf, C., G. Schnitkey, J. Coppess, N. Paulson, and K. Swanson. "Ad Hoc Payments: A Leading Indicator of Farm Policy Change." *farmdoc daily* 10, no. 140. (July 2020): 1. https://farmdocdaily.illinois.edu/2020/07/ad-hoc-payments-a-leading-indicator-of-farm-policy-change.html.

CHAPTER 9 | THE REST OF US

Amelinckx, Andrew. "5 Billionaires with Ties to Agriculture and Why They Do It." *Modern Farmer*, November 3, 2015. https://modernfarmer.com/2015/11/billionaire-farmers/.

Benshosan, April. "50 'Small' Food Brands That Are Actually Owned by Large Companies." *Eat This, Not That!*, June 28, 2018. https://www.eatthis.com/big-food-own-small-companies/.

Cain, Lisa. "Natural Jif: What's the Dif?" *Snack Girl* (blog). August 25, 2010. https://snack-girl.com/snack/natural-peanut-butter-ingredie/.

Graber, Roy. "Gallup: Agriculture Is the Most Trusted Industry in the U.S." *WATT Poultry* (blog). Apr. 20, 2021. https://www.wattagnet.com/blogs/27-agrifood-angle/post/42688-gallup-agriculture-is-most-trusted-industry-in-us.

Holt-Giménez, Eric. "We Already Grow Enough Food for 10 Billion People — And Still Can't End Hunger." *Huff Post*, December 18, 2014. https://www.huffpost.com/entry/world-hunger_b_1463429.

Jacobs, Tom. "The Downside of Farmers Markets." *Pacific Standard*, June 14, 2017. https://psmag.com/social-justice/the-down-side-of-farmers-markets.

Jayasinghe, Indika. "Customer Decision Making Criteria and the Importance of Price." Stax Insights on *Medium*, Oct 24, 2016. https://medium.com/stax-insights/consumer-decision-making-criteria-and-the-importance-of-price-1783d5589a8e.

Pollan, Michael. "Voting with Your Fork." *The New York Times* *"On the Table"* (blog). May 7, 2006. https://michaelpollan.com/articles-archive/voting-with-your-fork/.

Schwartz, Nelson D., and Coral Murphy Marcos, "Higher Food Prices Hit the Poor and Those Who Help Them." *The New York Times*, Oct. 27, 2021. https://www.nytimes.com/2021/10/27/business/economy/food-prices-us.html.

Smith, J. Travis. "The Real Story behind Big Beer's Ingredient War." *Gear Patrol*, February 15, 2019. https://www.gearpatrol.com/home/a551590/bud-light-miller-coors-corn-syrup/.

Soper, Taylor. "Here's Why Microsoft Just Invested $1.5m in a North Dakota High-Tech Farm Project." *GeekWire*, October 17, 2019. https://www.geekwire.com/2019/heres-microsoft-just-invested-1-5m-north-dakota-high-tech-farm-project/.

USDA ERS (United States Department of Agriculture Economic Research Service). *Food Prices and Spending*. Last updated December 27, 2021. https://www.ers.usda.gov/data-products/ag-and-food-statistics-charting-the-essentials/food-prices-and-spending/.

U.S. Farmers and Ranchers Alliance. "Nationwide Surveys Reveal Disconnect between Americans and Their Food." *Cision PR Newswire*, September 22, 2011. https://www.prnewswire.com/news-releases/nationwide-surveys-reveal-disconnect-between-americans-and-their-food-130336143.html.

Wallenfang, Maureen. "Half of Produce at Farm Stands Could Come from Grocery Stores." *USA Today*, June 23, 2017. https://

www.usatoday.com/story/news/nation-now/2017/06/21/
farm-stand-fakers-50-produce-could-come-grocery-stores/
415675001/.

Wells, Jeff. "12 Natural and Organic Brands Owned by Big Food."
Mental Floss, January 13, 2016. https://www.mentalfloss.com/
article/72624/12-natural-and-organic-brands-owned-big-food.

SELECTED FURTHER READING FOR BIG TEAM FARMS

Bowen, Sarah, Joslyn Brenton, and Sinikka Elliott. *Pressure Cooker: Why Home Cooking Won't Solve Our Problems and What We Can Do About It.* New York: Oxford University Press, 2019.

Brown, Adrianne Maree. *Emergent Strategy.* Chico: AK Press, 2017.

Curl, John. *For All the People: Uncovering the Hidden History of Cooperation, Cooperative Movements, and Communalism in America.* Oakland: PM Press, 2009.

Kimmerer, Robin Wall. *Braiding Sweetgrass: Indigenous Wisdom, Scientific Knowledge, and the Teachings of Plants.* Minneapolis: Milkweed Editions, 2013.

Kropotkin, Pëtr. *Fields, Factories and Workshops: or Industry Combined with Agriculture and Brain Work with Manual Work.* London: Thomas Nelson & Sons, 1912.

Linebaugh, Peter. *Stop Thief!: The Commons, Enclosures, and Resistance.* Oakland: PM Press, 2014.

Liu, Eric, and Nick Hanauer. *The Gardens of Democracy: A New American Story of Citizenship, the Economy, and the Role of Government*. Seattle: Sasquatch Books, 2011.

Matsumoto, Valerie J. *Farming the Home Place: A Japanese American Community in California 1919-1982*. Ithaca: Cornell University Press, 1993.

Mohawk, John, and José Barreiro. *Thinking in Indian: A John Mohawk Reader*. Golden: Fulcrum Publishing, 2010.

Nembhard, Jessica Gordon. *Collective Courage: A History of African American Cooperative Economic Thought and Practice*. University Park: Pennsylvania State University Press, 2014.

Pinchot, Elizabeth, and Gifford Pinchot. *The End of Bureaucracy and the Rise of the Intelligent Organization*. San Francisco: Berrett-Koehler Publishers, Inc., 1993.

Russell, Sharman Apt. *Hunger: An Unnatural History*. New York: Basic Books, 2005.

The Red Nation. *The Red Deal: Indigenous Action to Save Our Planet*. Brooklyn: Common Notions, 2021.

Trask, Haunani-Kay. *From a Native Daughter: Colonialism and Sovereignty in Hawai'i*. Honolulu: University of Hawai'i Press, 1999.

Yunkaporta, Tyson. *Sand Talk: How Indigenous Thinking Can Save the World*. New York: HarperCollins, 2020.